KT-557-233

Wordspinners

Barry Maybury

OXFORD UNIVERSITY PRESS 1981

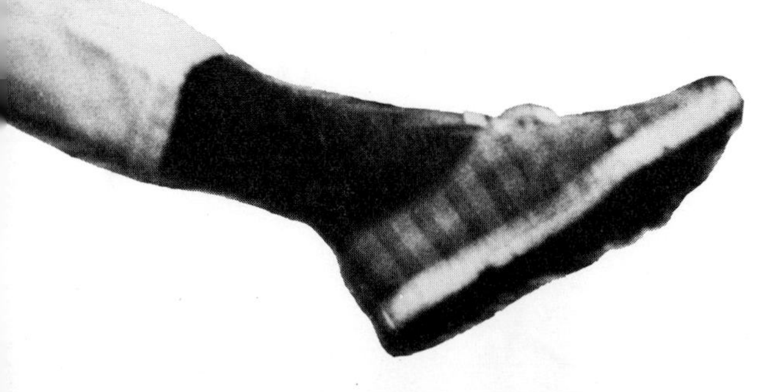

Oxford University Press, Walton Street, Oxford OX2 6DP

OXFORD LONDON GLASGOW
NEW YORK TORONTO MELBOURNE WELLINGTON
KUALA LUMPUR SINGAPORE HONG KONG TOKYO
DELHI BOMBAY CALCUTTA MADRAS KARACHI
NAIROBI DAR ES SALAAM CAPE TOWN

ISBN 0 19 833158 4

Companion anthologies compiled by Barry Maybury:

Wordscapes ISBN 0 19 833138 X
Thoughtshapes ISBN 0 19 833141 X
Thoughtweavers ISBN 0 19 833159 2

Set in Great Britain by
Fakenham Press Limited, Fakenham, Norfolk
Printed in Hong Kong

Contents

* written by a child at school

Words . . . Poems

Look after
the
and the
            will
take care
of themselves

ROGER McGOUGH

My Poem

If air had a shadow,
There would be no silhouettes,
The sky would be grey all day,
And pitch black at night.
No smoke be seen from chimneys
No motes in the streams of sun
The fox would hunt at daybreak
The owl would supper at noon,
The lights in all our windows
Would be like a thousand moons.

ALEXANDER JOHNSTON*

Winter Walk

Take the street where the cinders crunch,
where a leaning gaslamp's splinters
haunt a cat's eyes, green as bile,
cold as the winter's.
While the heavy shoulders hunch,
and the soot-stained snowflakes pile,
hear the voices in the air:
'These streets lead nowhere, nowhere.'
Summon the echoes from the brew:
no one, not a soul, will bother.
Flagstoned ages lie beyond
this frozen smother.
And the streets you thought you knew
shift, and break the easy bond,
hear the voices in the air:
'These streets lead nowhere, nowhere.'

Every house is bolted tight,
every street has slipped its tether,
all the world's gone to its bed
but you and the weather.
No wise men will come tonight,
not a star shine overhead.
Hear the voices in the air:
'These streets lead nowhere, nowhere.'

TONY CONNOR

brew: steep street

Event

Nothing is happening
Nothing

A waterdrop
Soundlessly shatters
A gossamer gives

Against this unused space
A bird
Might thoughtlessly try its voice
But no bird does

On the trodden ground
Footsteps
Are themselves more pulse than sound

At the return
A little drunk
On air

Aware that
Nothing
Is happening

CHARLES TOMLINSON

The Old Alley

Soaked papers cling to aged stone,
Dustbin lids rock to and fro in the light wind,
Milk cartons, beer bottles and newspapers
Squeeze through holed, rusty and overloaded bins.
Broken drainpipes hang from decaying and depressing walls,
Thieving rats raid abandoned houses.
'Mick for Trace' chalked on to a wall
Now blurred and hanging limply
As specks of drizzle touch the writing.
A malodorous smell reeks from open drains,
Shattered windows reveal dark and musty places behind.
Shadows hang dolefully on cracked brick,
The echoes of children playing bounces back off
Each alley wall.
A homeless dog limps in the gutter,
Sniffing at the drains—whining for food.
The drizzle stops.
Rays of sun try to grope their way into
Sheltered corners of this dark, musty, alley-way.

I look on, thinking of the past,
The good old past,
I feel no emotions,
I can't,
Ghosts can't.
I am just an old forgotten stranger,
Drifting through this wise abandoned alley.

RICHARD PARTRIDGE*

The Roadmen

The roadmen have come again,
To dig the road,
To repair the pipes,
With their tin-made hut
And cups of tea.

BRIAN POOLE*

Auto Wreck

Its quick soft silver bell beating, beating,
And down the dark one ruby flare
Pulsing out red light like an artery,
The ambulance at top speed floating down
Past beacons and illuminated clocks
Wings in a heavy curve, dips down,
And brakes speed, entering the crowd.
The doors leap open, emptying light;
Stretchers are laid out, the mangled lifted
And stowed into the little hospital.
Then the bell, breaking the hush, tolls once,
And the ambulance with its terrible cargo
Rocking, slightly rocking, moves away,
As the doors, an afterthought, are closed.

KARL SHAPIRO

The Borehole

A huddle of iron jammy-cranes
Straddles the skear, shanks
Rusty from salt rains,
Or half-way up their barnacled flanks
In the flood tide. Paid-up pits
Lounge round the banks,
Turning out red pockets.
The cranking waders stand,
Necks down, bills grinding in their sockets,
Drilling the sand.
A steam-pipe whistles, the clanged iron bells;
Five hundred feet of limestone shudders and
Creaks down all its strata'd spine of ammonites and shells

And a vertical worm of stone is worried
Out from the earth's core.
The daylight falls
Westward with the ebb, before
The night-shift buzzer calls:
But what is it sticks in the bird's gullet—
Rubble or crystal, dross or ore?

NORMAN NICHOLSON

jammy-cranes: herons
skear: a bank of shingle or stones exposed at low tide

Rain

The drenched banana skin
Floats down the drain.
The grid stops it and its skin
Opens out like an octopus.

STUART BRIDGES*

Dandelion

Sure as a soldier to find the best place,
Dig down deep and then spread out
A green, split groundsheet; a coarse, cheerful face,
Never fresh yellow, on a deceptive neck
Staffed with reinforcements; yellow job soon done,
Consolidates, constructs a startling wig
As decoy for the winds to take;
Sticks the fuzz aboveground, waits.
Platoons of sons are whirled away to dig . . .

Stiff bald fathers with coarse-pored pates
See to wider billets for their groundsheets.

P. J. KAVANAGH

Dewdrops

The dewdrops on every blade of grass are so much like silver drops that I am obliged to stoop down as I walk to see if they are pearls, and those sprinkled on the ivy-woven beds of primroses underneath the hazels, whitethorns, and maples are so like gold beads that I stooped down to feel if they were hard, but they melted from my finger. And where the dew lies on the primrose, the violet and whitethorn leaves, they are emerald and beryl, yet nothing more than the dews of the morning on the budding leaves; nay, the road grasses are covered with gold and silver beads, and the further we go the brighter they seem to shine, like solid gold and silver. It is nothing more than the sun's light and shade upon them in the dewy morning; every thorn-point and every bramble-spear has its trembling ornament: till the wind gets a little brisker, and then all is shaken off, and all the shining jewelry passes away into a common spring morning full of budding leaves, primroses, violets, vernal speedwell, bluebell and orchis, and commonplace objects.

John Clare

Water Picture

In the pond in the park
all things are doubled:
Long buildings hang and
wriggle gently. Chimneys
are bent legs bouncing
on clouds below. A flag
wags like a fish-hook
down there in the sky.

The arched stone bridge
is an eye, with underlid
in the water. In its lens
dip crinkled heads with hats
that don't fall off. Dogs go by,
barking on their backs . . .

Treetops deploy a haze of
cherry bloom for roots,
where birds coast belly-up
in the glass bowl of a hill . . .

A swan, with twin necks
forming the figure three,
steers between two dimpled
towers doubled. Fondly,
hissing, she kisses herself,
and all the scene is troubled:
water-windows splinter,
tree-limbs tangle, the bridge
folds like a fan.

MAY SWENSON

Rainbow Stuff

'That blessed child and her fairies,' said Gran, shaking her head over the washtub.

'But Gran.' She clutched the rag doll and looked up into Gran's red face.

'Go and play now, love.'

Milly went out, pulling the doll's shabby string hair back over its head, muttering to herself.

'*I* know. . . .' After all she had seen their rainbow stuff on the pools after the rain, and one day when Grandad had taken her for a walk he had swung her round onto his shoulders, staggering and bumping into the wall pretending he couldn't see because she had pulled his cap down over his eyes. And then, over the wall she could see it. It was beautiful, full of tall grass and wildflowers, bushes and a lake covered with the bright rainbow stuff shimmering in the sun.

'Stop, Grandad, stop! I can see fairyland. . . .' But he started running, jogging her on his shoulders.

She went out taking the doll's blanket and the little stool for a table and the old dolls' pram. The others came across the yard—Betty and Dorothy and Joycey and they played on the steps. But after a while there was an argument and the others started to go away. She sat miserably pulling the doll's hair. But just before they went down the entry she said suddenly:

'I know where fairyland is.'

'No such place.'

'There is so.'

'No, there ain't. You make things up you do.'

'All right, then, I'll show you.'

They pushed the dolls' pram down the street as she led the way, the others trailing behind.

The high brick wall was a good way down the road past the Co-op and the Frog Hall and over the railway bridge.

'Here,' she said at last, turning down the snicket. 'It's over there.'

'It's the gasworks,' said the twins. 'Our George works here.'

'No, it isn't,' she insisted. 'You look over there then and you'll see the rainbow stuff, and the flowers and everything.'

Betty made a back and Joycey scrambled up where part of the wall had fallen away.

'Cor then!' she said. 'It is an' all.' Dorothy hauled herself up and sat astride the wall. By standing on the pram the others dragged themselves alongside. Then they all jumped down into the mass of tangled grass, willowherb and golden tansy, and giggling at their boldness they began to pick bunches of the flowers. For a while they forgot what they had come for until Milly said:

'What about the rainbow stuff?'

'Come on, let's get some,' Betty said, running up to the edge of the black lake. The rainbow sheen was spread out over the still surface.

It was a bit muddy round the edge and they couldn't easily reach the gaudy colours so they began to wade out, stretching forward. They sank up to their knees in the slime and bubbles of unpleasant smelling gas began to pop up.

'My feet's stuck,' said Betty, half giggling and half crying.

Joycey stumbled and had the black shiny stuff over her face and hair. She began to bawl. Then they all started yelling and screaming, floundering about in the oily iridescent mud. The more they struggled the more they got it onto their dresses and arms. Soon three small girls were transformed into dribbling mad imps.

But then a cap and a face appeared over the wall. It was grandad.

'Well, I goo to our 'ouse!' He scaled the wall and was soon dragging out the squarking children.

'I don't know what yer gran'll mek of this, I'm hanged if I do.' Milly had lost her shoe and Betty's hair was plastered to her face. The doll was a greasy blueblack lump.

When they got home Milly was scrubbed clean and put to bed in disgrace. But later on when it was dusk and the fire was lit Grandad brought her down and sat her on the hearth.

'Whatever possessed you to goo in the gasworks?' he said, not unkindly.

'We went to see. . . .' she couldn't say it.

'Yes?'

'It was the rainbow stuff,' she tried to explain. 'All shiny on the lake.'

'Oh, you mean the *oil*. It were the colours took yer fancy, then, were it?' He poked the fire. 'Well, I don't expect you'll be goin' theer awhile.'

Tears began to run down her cheeks.

'Come on, now, it's all over.'

'But I thought. . . .'

'What did yer think?'

'Nothing.'

The old man's eyes searched the child's.

'I thought it was fairyland, Grandad,' she said quietly.

'Oh, I see,' he said. 'Fairyland, eh. Well.' There was a silence and both of them looked into the fire. Then he picked the child up and sat her on his lap.

'Well, now,' he said thoughtfully. ''Appen it were.'

She turned and looked up into his face to see if he was making fun of her.

''Appen it were. Only the mistek you made, my love, was ter try and grab 'old on it, see.'

The child pondered on this.

The old man went on:

'Now summat like that, well, yo' can't lay yer 'and on. No, my word you can't. Nor yer foot neither.'

He took out his pipe and stuffed the dark tobacco in chuckling to himself. Then he lit the pipe and puffed away contentedly. The fire crackled and the clock ticked.

''Cause if everybody tried to grab a bit an' just keep it like for theirsen, well, my word, there wouldn't be enough to go around.'

He blew out clouds of blue smoke which rose gently in the kitchen.

'Yer see, love, there's got to be a bit for everybody.' He took the pipe out of his mouth and winked.

''Asn't there?'

The child rested her head against the old man's shoulder and sighed contentedly.

'Yes,' she said.

JOAN GUEST

The Scullery

The scullery was a mine of all the minerals of living. Here I discovered water—a very different element from the green crawling scum that stank in the garden tub. You could pump it in pure blue gulps out of the ground, you could swing on the pump handle and it came out sparkling like liquid sky. And it broke and ran and shone on the tiled floor, or quivered in a jug, or weighted your clothes with cold. You could drink it, draw with it, froth it with soap, swim beetles across it, or fly it in bubbles in the air. You could put your head in it, and open your eyes, and see the sides of the bucket buckle, and hear your caught breath roar, and work your mouth like a fish, and smell the lime from the ground. Substance of magic—which you could tear or wear, confine or scatter, or send down holes, but never burn or break or destroy.

The scullery was water, where the old pump stood. And it had everything else that was related to water: thick steam of Mondays edgy with starch; soapsuds boiling, bellying and popping, creaking and whispering, rainbowed with light and winking with a million windows. Bubble bubble, toil and grumble, rinsing and slapping of sheets and shirts, and panting Mother rowing her red arms like oars in the steaming waves. Then the linen came up on a stick out of the pot, like pastry, or woven suds, or sheets of moulded snow.

from Cider with Rosie by LAURIE LEE

The Washing Machine

It goes fwunkety,
 then shlunkety,
as the washing goes around.

The water spluncheses
 and it sluncheses,
as the washing goes around.

As you pick it out it splocheses,
 then it flocheses,
as the washing goes around.

But at the end it schlopperies,
 and then flopperies,
and the washing stops going round.

JEFFREY DAVIES*

Clocks

... slow clocks, quick clocks, pendulumed heart-knocks, china, alarm, grandfather, cuckoo; clocks shaped like Noah's whirring Ark, clocks that bicker in marble ships, clocks in the wombs of glass women, hourglass chimers, tu-wit-tu-woo clocks, clocks that pluck tunes, Vesuvius clocks all black bells and lava, Niagara clocks that cataract their ticks, old time-weeping clocks with ebony beards, clocks with no hands for ever drumming out time without ever knowing what time it is.

from Under Milk Wood by DYLAN THOMAS

The Wooden Stag

The teak wooden stag
In the living room
Stood on the fireplace
On its own,
As if it was forgotten.
It was surrounded
By a half a dozen
Wooden shelves,
With a few books
Upon them,
Which made up
The whole fireplace surrounding.

Below the stag
Glowed the bright
Orange, yellow flames
Of the magicoal fire,
Sending out imaginary heat
Which you are amazed at.

CARL MURRAY

Along the Seashore

The grainy sand had gone from under his feet. His boots trod again a damp crackling mast, razorshells, squeaking pebbles, that on the unnumbered pebbles beats, wood sieved by the shipworm, lost Armada. Unwholesome sandflats waited to suck his treading soles, breathing upward sewage breath. He coasted them, walking warily. A porterbottle stood up, stogged to its waist, in the cakely sand dough. A sentinel: isle of dreadful thirst. Broken hoops on the shore; at the land a maze of dark cunning nets; farther away chalkscrawled backdoors and on the higher beach a dryingline with two crucified shirts.

from Ulysses by JAMES JOYCE

Stone Speech

Crowding this beach
are milkstones, white
teardrops; flints
edged out of flinthood
into smoothness chafe
against grainy ovals,
pitted pieces, nosestones,
stoppers and saddles;
veins of orange
inlay black beads:
chalk-swaddled babyshapes,
tiny fists, facestones
and facestone's brother
skullstones, roundheads
pierced by a single eye,
purple finds, all
rubbing shoulders:
a mob of grindings,
groundlings, scatterings
from a million necklaces
mined under sea-hills, the pebbles
are as various as the people.

CHARLES TOMLINSON

The World Below the Brine

The world below the brine,
Forests at the bottom of the sea, the branches and leaves,
Sea-lettuce, vast lichens, strange flowers and seeds,
  the thick tangle, openings, and pink turf,
Different colours, pale gray and green, purple, white,
  and gold, the play of light through the water,
Dumb swimmers there among the rocks, coral, gluten,
  grass, rushes, and the aliment of the swimmers,
Sluggish existences grazing there suspended, or slowly
  crawling close to the bottom,
The sperm-whale at the surface blowing air and spray
  or disporting with his flukes,
The leaden-eyed shark, the walrus, the turtle, the
  hairy sea-leopard, and the sting ray,
Passions there, wars, pursuits, tribes, sight in
  those ocean-depths, breathing that thick-breathing air,
  as so many do,
The change thence to the sight here, and to the subtle
  air breathed by beings like us who walk this sphere,
The change onward from ours to that of beings who walk
  other spheres.

WALT WHITMAN

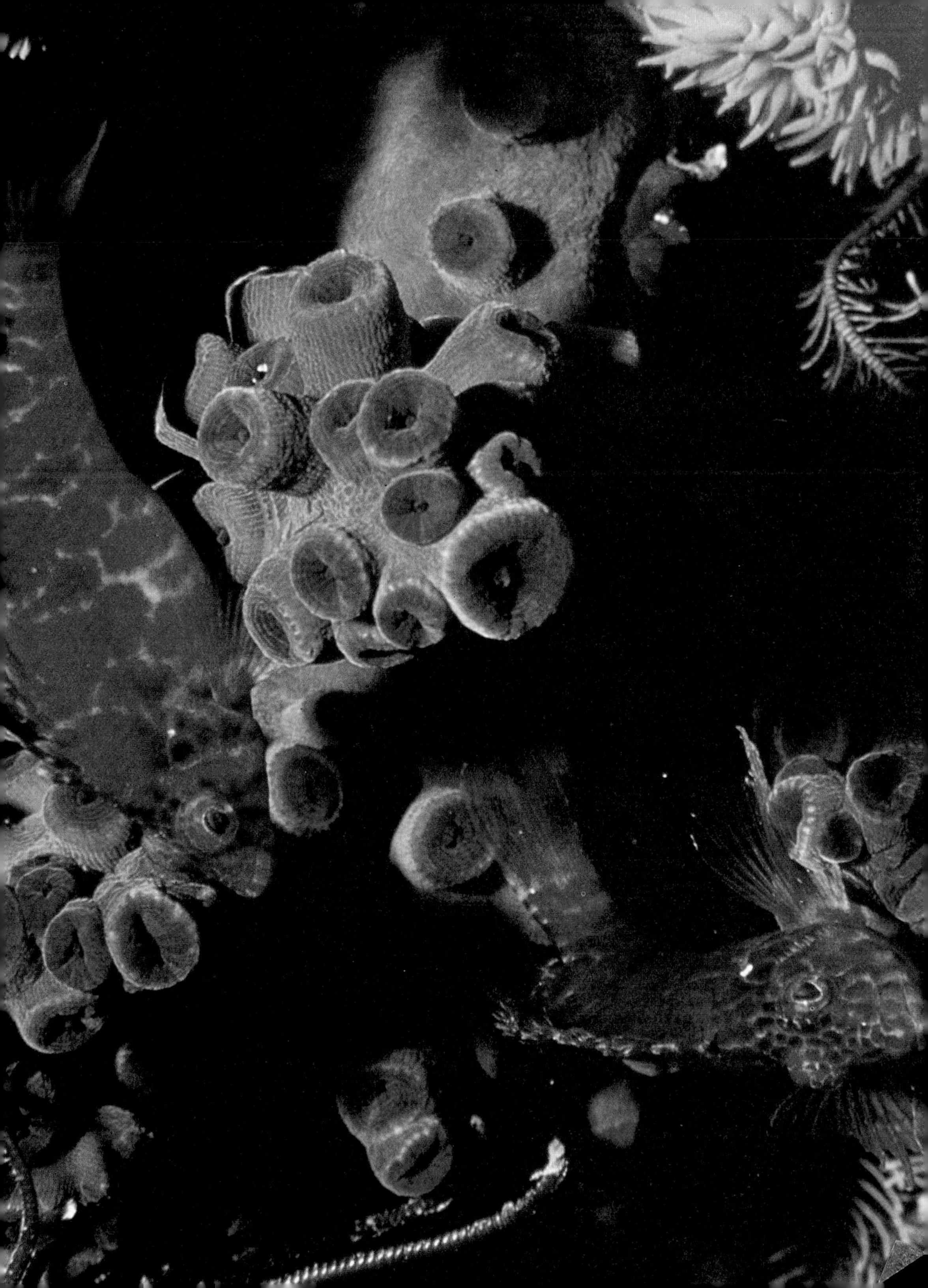

Conger Eel

He was eight feet long. At the centre of his back he was two feet in circumference. Slipping sinuously along the bottom of the sea at a gigantic pace, his black mysterious body glistened and twirled like a wisp in a foaming cataract. His little eyes, stationed wide apart in his flat-boned, broad skull, searched the ocean for food. He coursed ravenously for miles along the base of the range of cliffs. He searched fruitlessly except for three baby pollocks which he swallowed in one mouthful without arresting his progress. He was very hungry.

Then he turned by a sharp promontory and entered a cliff-bound harbour where the sea was dark and silent, shaded by the concave cliffs. Savagely he looked ahead into the dark waters. Then instantaneously he flicked his tail, rippling his body like a twisted screw, and shot forward. His long, thin, single whisker, hanging from his lower snout like a label tag, jerked back under his belly. His glassy eyes rested ferociously on the minute spots that scurried about in the sea a long distance ahead. The conger eel had sighted his prey. There was a school of mackerel a mile away.

He came upon them headlong, in a flash. He rose out of the deep from beneath their white bellies, and gripped one mackerel in his wide-open jaws ere his snout met the surface. Then, as if in a swoon, his body went limp, and tumbling over and over, convulsing like a crushed worm, he sank lower and lower until at last he had swallowed the fish. Then immediately he straightened out and flicked his tail, ready to pursue his prey afresh.

The school of mackerel, when the dread monster had appeared among them, were swimming just below the surface of the sea. When the eel rushed up they had hurled themselves clean out of the water with the sound of innumerable grains of sand being shaken in an immense sieve. The thousand blue and white bodies flashed and shimmered in the sun for three moments, and then they disappeared, leaving a large patch of the dark water convulsing turbulently. Ten thousand little fins cut the surface of the sea as the mackerel set off in a headlong flight. Their white bellies were no longer visible. They plunged down into the depths of the sea, where their blue-black sides and backs, the colour of the sea, hid them from their enemy. The eel surged about in immense figures of eight; but he had lost them.

Half-hungry, half-satisfied, he roamed about for half an hour, a demented giant of the deep, travelling restlessly at an incredible speed. Then at last his little eyes again sighted his prey. Little white spots again hung like faded drops of brine in the sea ahead of him. He rushed thither. He opened his jaws as the spots assumed shape, and then loomed up close to his eyes. But just as he attempted to gobble the nearest one, he felt a savage impact. Then something hard and yet intangible pressed against his head and then down along his back. He leaped and turned somersault. The hard gripping material completely enveloped him. He was in a net. While on all sides of him mackerel wriggled gasping in the meshes.

The eel paused for two seconds amazed and terrified. Then all around him he saw a web of black strands hanging miraculously in the water, everywhere, while mackerel with heaving gills stood rigid and their bodies curved in an arch, others encompassed many times in the uneven folds, others girdled firmly below the gills with a single black thread. Glittering, they eddied back and forth with the stream of the sea, a mass of fish being strangled in the deep.

Then the eel began to struggle fiercely to escape. He hurtled hither and thither, swinging his long slippery body backwards and forwards, ripping with his snout, surging forward suddenly at full speed, churning the water. He ripped and tore the net, cutting great long gashes in it. But the more he cut and ripped the more deeply enmeshed did he become. He did not release himself, but he released some of the mackerel. They fell from the torn meshes, stiff and crippled, downwards, sinking like dead things. Then suddenly one after another they seemed to awake from sleep, shook their tails, and darted away while the giant eel was gathering coil upon coil of the net about his slippery body. Then, at last, exhausted and half-strangled, he lay still, heaving.

Presently he felt himself being hauled up in the net. The net crowded around him more, so that the little gleaming mackerel, imprisoned with him, rubbed his sides and lay soft and flabby against him, all hauled up in the net with him. He lay still. He reached the surface and gasped, but he made no movement. Then he was hauled heavily into a boat, and fell with a thud into the bottom.

The two fishermen in the boat began to curse violently when they saw the monstrous eel that had torn their net and ruined their catch of mackerel. The old man on the oars in the boat called out: 'Free him and kill him, the brute.' The young man who was hauling in the net looked in terror at the slippery monster that lay between his feet, with its little eyes looking up cunningly, as if it were human. He almost trembled as he picked up the net and began to undo the coils. 'Slash it with your knife,' yelled the old man, 'before he does more harm.' The young man picked up his knife from the gunwale where it was stuck, and cut the net, freeing the eel. The eel, with sudden and amazing movement, glided up the bottom of the boat, so that he stretched full length.

Then he doubled back, rocking the boat as he beat the sides with his whirling tail, his belly flopping in the water that lay in the bottom. The two men screamed, both crying, 'Kill him, or he'll drown us!' 'Strike him on the nable!' They both reached for the short, thick stick that hung from a peg amidships. The young man grabbed it, bent down, and struck the eel. 'Hit him on the nable,' cried the old man; 'catch him, catch him, and turn him over.'

They both bent down, pawing at the eel, cursing and panting, while the boat rocked ominously and the huge conger eel glided around and around at an amazing speed. Their hands clawed his sides, slipping over them like skates on ice. They gripped him with their knees, they stood on him, they tried to lie on him, but in their confusion they could not catch him.

Then at last the young man lifted him up in his arms, holding him in the middle, gripping him as if he were trying to crush him to death. He staggered upwards. 'Now strike him on the nable!' he yelled to the old man. But suddenly he staggered backwards. The boat rocked. He dropped the eel with an oath, reaching out with his hands to steady himself. The eel's head fell over the canted gunwale. His snout dipped into the sea. With an immense shiver he glided away, straight down to the depths, down like an arrow, until he reached the dark, weed-covered rocks at the bottom.

Then, stretching out to his full length he coursed in a wide arc to his enormous lair, far away in the silent depths.

LIAM O'FLAHERTY

Little Fish

The tiny fish enjoy themselves
in the sea
Quick little splinters of life,
their little lives are fun to them
in the sea.

D. H. LAWRENCE

Legend

I saw three ships go sailing by,
Over the sea, the lifting sea,
And the wind rose in the morning sky,
And one was rigged for a long journey.

The first ship turned towards the west,
Over the sea, the running sea,
And by the wind was all possessed
And carried to a rich country.

The second turned towards the east,
Over the sea, the quaking sea,
And the wind hunted it like a beast
To anchor in captivity.

The third ship drove towards the north,
Over the sea, the darkening sea,
But no breath of wind came forth,
And the decks shone frostily.

The northern sky rose high and black
Over the proud unfruitful sea,
East and west the ships came back
Happily or unhappily:

But the third went wide and far
Into an unforgiving sea
Under a fire-spilling star,
And it was rigged for a long journey.

PHILIP LARKIN

Jonathan Seagull

From a thousand feet, flapping his wings as hard as he could, he pushed over into a blazing steep dive towards the waves, and learned why seagulls don't make blazing steep power-dives. In just six seconds he was moving seventy miles per hour, the speed at which one's wing goes unstable on the upstroke.

Time after time it happened. Careful as he was, working at the very peak of his ability, he lost control at high speed.

Climb to a thousand feet. Full power straight ahead first, then push over, flapping, to a vertical dive. Then, every time, his left wing stalled on an upstroke, he'd roll violently left, stall his right wing recovering, and flick like fire into a wild tumbling spin to the right.

He couldn't be careful enough on that upstroke. Ten times he tried, and all ten times, as he passed through seventy miles per hour, he burst into a churning mass of feathers, out of control, crashing down into the water.

The key, he thought at last, dripping wet, must be to hold the wings still at high speeds—then flap up to fifty and then hold the wings still.

From two thousand feet he tried again, rolling into his dive, beak straight down, wings full out and stable from the moment he passed fifty miles per hour. It took tremendous strength, but it worked. In ten seconds he had blurred through ninety miles per hour. Jonathan had set a world record for seagulls!

from Jonathan Livingstone Seagull by RICHARD BACH

The Sea

The sea is splashing,
spraying, tumbling.
The spray is so powerful,
Gigantic waves come tumbling
over the ship.
The force of the waves,
The sea splashing against the ship,
almighty waves so big.
And then gradually
the storm dies away,
Then everything
is quiet again.

RICHARD BLOXAM*

Light

The light is like a spider.
It crawls over the water.
It crawls over the edges of the snow.
It crawls under your eyelids
And spreads its webs there—
Its two webs.

WALLACE STEVENS

Wind and Rain

Like Rain it sounded till it curved
And then I knew 'twas Wind—
It walked as wet as any Wave
But swept as dry as sand—
When it had pushed itself away
To some remotest Plain
A coming as of Hosts was heard
That was indeed the Rain—
It filled the Wells, it pleased the Pools
It warbled in the Road—
It pulled the spigot from the Hills
And let the Floods abroad,—
It loosened acres, lifted seas
The sites of Centres stirred
Then like Elijah rode away
Upon a Wheel of Cloud.

EMILY DICKINSON

Hurricane Flora

On September the thirtieth 1963, I had the most memorable experience of my life. This is a live story of how it all happened.

On the beautiful morning of September the thirtieth, I, because of illness (influenza), stayed away from school. The morning was bright and sunny, but slightly windy. My three brothers had actually gone to school, so Vernon, a cousin of mine, my younger sister Linda, my mother and I were at home.

All of a sudden the wind began increasing and so I began to question my mother, 'Mammy, did storm ever come in Tobago?' I asked. 'Yesson, once when you was a little baby,' she said. 'But Mammy, look like a storm, look how the banana trees falling down,' I said. 'Boy don't talk stupidness, eh.' But the wind continued increasing. Then I heard Mammy's voice saying, 'Boy it look as though yuh talking truth, yes. We better go upstairs.'

By the time we were upstairs and finished closing the windows, there was a resounding crash. The avocado tree, laden with beautiful fruit had fallen about two yards from the northern side of the house.

Coconut trees all around the house kept falling, some of their heads twisted as though the mighty hand of some unseen giant kept wringing them. Limbs of the cedar and bayleaf tree were being hurled like arrows through the air. There was a deathly calm.

At about one p.m. the first part of the hurricane had passed, and the principal of the elementary school urged all students to try to get home before the second half struck. Fortunately my elder brother reached home in time.

Vernon and I, at the interval of the hurricane, went out to the back yard to gather coconuts (water nuts) for drinking purposes when the second half came.

The second half of the hurricane came from the south-east just opposite to the first part; it came with a terrific force and a spinning motion, at about 120 m.p.h. The noise the wind made was like that of a jet plane whistling through the air.

In front of our house there are two large cedars and a bayleaf tree. Had it not been for these trees our house would have been destroyed. Like a boy raising the roof of his toy house, half of the roof of the shop which is also in front of the house came flying through the air and smashed with unbelievable force against the cedars and bayleaf tree. It wrapped neatly around the trees like the hand of a man around match sticks.

The wind continued blowing with sheets of rain splashing against the house. Just to say how strong the wind was, Vernon and I went downstairs. When we opened the door both of us together could not close it back because of the force of the wind.

The wind decreased slowly after its destroying work was finished.

Nine people died, four-fifths of the houses were either destroyed completely or damaged. At the end of the hurricane, the island looked as though bombs had been dropped ten feet apart all over the island.

*anonymous Tobagan boy**

Hurricane

A hurricane is a hotfoot in great haste, giving an uproar of violence, a nomad roaming from place to place, leaving distress and sorrow, leaving people perplexed and bewildered, leaving damage indescribable. It looks like a storm on the sea, all pucker, leaving wrinkles and folds, a revolution getting revenge for some unsettled score, causing riot everywhere. It looks like a scrawny piece of cloth ragged and ripped, until now kept remote and undisturbing, secluded.

DAVID HOSELL*

Hen Feeding

The clocking hen puffed out her feathers and sounded a sharp, throaty *cluck*. With her mottled tan and white plumage raised from her body she seemed twice her real size. As she strutted a few steps forward in an attitude of special authority she clucked again and called her scampering brood of chicks in behind her. With a single movement of her claw she scratched the earth vigorously, then danced back two rapid steps, bending her beak and eyes quickly to the ground. Finding an earthworm, she raised her head and began a monotonous sequence of high insistent peeping noises, calling her chicks to the food. Only when they had all gathered in to her did she bend her beak again, seize the worm and begin tearing it apart with rapid shakings of her head. A plain white hen, hearing the shrill sounds, abandoned her scratching a few yards away and ran over to join the meal—unwary! Quickly the clocking hen puffed herself out even more broadly than before and, whirling suddenly, raced at the white hen, pecking at her head and crying out menacingly as she did so. As the white hen fled in alarm the clocker turned back to her brood and led them a few steps further off. . . .

For three weeks she would lie on the eggs, elaborately puffed out, careful to bring them all under the warmth of her body and her canopied feathers, seldom leaving the nest even for food, generating a feverish warmth. Then for six weeks more she would guard the chicks, lead them about, clucking them after her, teaching them to scratch, calling them to food, sheltering them at night and protecting them fiercely. The rooster himself, twice the weight and size of the hen, quickly learned to leave her and her chosen feeding grounds alone, and even the farm's dogs and cats stayed well away. For nine weeks in all the hen would achieve feats of vigour and courage and bluff she was quite unequal to the rest of the year. Then one day, very suddenly, she would lose the drive to clock, her plumage would collapse and she would return to her normal size. Back feeding with the other hens she would submit to their pecking and domination until she found her natural place again in the flock. Eventually even the chicks of her own brood, reaching full size nine months later, would face her one by one and test themselves against her.

from The Hired Man by ROBERT BERNAN

Farrier's Dog

Here's one dog won't get under horse's hoofs;
he sits, haunched-up attention, by the forge,
belly like bellows and tooth-printed tongue.

His master heats and hammers soft pink iron,
chimes nail-holes through; dog blinks through parted air;
horse flicks its flank, sweats, lights a livid eye.

The man slaps its taut neck, hefts up its foot
against his thigh and with a quick knife pares
hoof-rind away; the dog whines silently.

The red shoe is by burning bedded in;
from out a thick gout of ammonia smoke
and thin steam spurting when the shoe is quenched

a mess of parings comes, kicked to the dog
who in crouched, greedy spasms gulps it down;
iron is hammered home, and the horse stamps.

PAUL HYLAND

Little City

Spider, from his flaming sleep,
staggers out into the window frame;
swings out from the red den where he slept
to nest in the gnarled glass.

Fat hero, burnished cannibal
lets down a frail ladder and ties a knot,
sways down to a landing with furry grace.

By noon this corner is a bullet-coloured city
and the exhausted architect
sleeps in his pale wheel,
waits without pity for a gold visitor
or coppery captive, his aerial enemies
spinning headlong down the window to the trap.

The street of string shakes now and announces
a surprised angel in the tunnel of thread.
Spider dances down his wiry heaven to taste the moth.
A little battle begins and the prison trembles.
The round spider hunches like a judge.
The wheel glistens.
But this transparent town that caves in at a breath
is paved with perfect steel.
The victim hangs by his feet, and the spider
circles invisible avenues, weaving a grave.

By evening the web is heavy with monsters,
bright constellation of wasps and bees,
breathless, surrendered.

Bronze skeletons dangle on the wires
and a thin wing flutters.
The medieval city hangs in its stars.

Spider lumbers down the web
and the city stretches with the weight of his walking.
By night we cannot see the flies' faces
and the spider, rocking.

ROBERT HORAN

Silent Gliding

Wake the serpent not—lest he
Should not know the way to go,—
Let him crawl which yet lies sleeping
Through the deep grass of the meadow!
Not a bee shall hear him creeping,
Not a may-fly shall awaken
From its cradling blue-bell shaken,
Not the starlight as he's sliding
Through the grass with silent gliding.

P. B. SHELLEY

Lizard

A lizard ran out on a rock and looked up, listening
no doubt to the sounding of the spheres.
And what a dandy fellow! the right toss of a chin for you
and swirl of a tail!

If men were as much men as lizards are lizards
they'd be worth looking at.

D. H. LAWRENCE

The Red Cockatoo

Sent as a present from Annam—
A red cockatoo.
Coloured like the peach-tree blossom,
Speaking with the speech of men.
And they did to it what is always done
To the learned and eloquent.
They took a cage with stout bars
And shut it up inside.

PO CHÜ-I
Translated from Chinese by Arthur Waley

The Puppy

In our backyard a boy keeps his little Sharik chained up, a ball of fluff shackled since he was a puppy.

One day I took him some chicken bones that were still warm and smelt delicious. The boy had just let the poor dog off his lead to have a run round the yard. The snow there was deep and feathery; Sharik was bounding about like a hare, first on his hind legs, then on his front ones, from one corner of the yard to the other, back and forth, burying his muzzle in the snow.

He ran towards me, his coat all shaggy, jumped up at me, sniffed the bones—then off he went again, belly-deep in the snow.

I don't need your bones, he said, just give me my freedon....

ALEXANDER SOLZHENITSYN
Translated from Russian by Michael Glenny

The Fox

The shepherd on his journey heard when nigh
His dog among the bushes barking high;
The ploughman ran and gave a hearty shout,
He found a weary fox and beat him out.
The ploughman laughed and would have ploughed him in,
But the old shepherd took him for the skin.
He lay upon the furrow stretched for dead,
The old dog lay and licked the wounds that bled,
The ploughman beat him till his ribs would crack,
And then the shepherd slung him at his back;
And when he rested, to his dog's surprise,
The old fox started from his dead disguise
And while the dog lay panting in the sedge
He up and snapt and bolted through the hedge.

He scampered to the bushes far away;
The shepherd called the ploughman to the fray;
The ploughman wished he had a gun to shoot.
The old dog barked and followed the pursuit.
The shepherd threw his hook and tottered past;
The ploughman ran, but none could go so fast;
The woodman threw his faggot from the way
And ceased to chop and wondered at the fray.
But when he saw the dog and heard the cry
He threw his hatchet—but the fox was by.
The shepherd broke his hook and lost the skin;
He found a badger-hole and bolted in.
They tried to dig, but, safe from danger's way,
He lived to chase the hounds another day.

JOHN CLARE

The Land Turtle

The concrete highway was edged with a mat of tangled, broken, dry grass, and the grass heads were heavy with oat beards to catch on a dog's coat, and foxtails to tangle in a horse's fetlocks, and clover burrs to fasten in sheep's wool; sleeping life waiting to be spread and dispersed, every seed armed with an appliance of dispersal, twisting darts and parachutes for the wind, little spears and balls of tiny thorns, and all waiting for animals and for the wind, for a man's trouser cuff or the hem of a woman's skirt, all passive but armed with appliances of activity, still, but each possessed of the anlage of movement.

The sun lay on the grass and warmed it, and in the shade under the grass the insects moved, ants and ant lions to set traps for them, grasshoppers to jump into the air and flick their yellow wings for a second, sow bugs like little armadillos, plodding restlessly on many tender feet. And over the grass at the roadside a land turtle crawled, turning aside for nothing, dragging his high-domed shell over the grass. His hard legs and yellow-nailed feet threshed slowly through the grass, not really walking, but boosting and dragging his shell along. The barley beards slid off his shell, and the clover burrs fell on him and rolled to the ground. His horny beak was partly open, and his fierce, humorous eyes, under brows like finger-nails, stared straight ahead. He came over the grass leaving a beaten trail behind him, and the hill, which was the highway embankment, reared up ahead of him. For a moment he stopped, his head held high. He blinked and looked up and down. At last he started to climb the embankment. Front clawed feet reached forward but did not touch. The hind feet kicked his shell along, and it scraped on the grass, and on the gravel. As the embankment grew steeper and steeper, the more frantic were the efforts of the land turtle. Pushing hind legs strained and slipped, boosting the shell along, and the horny head protruded as far as the neck could stretch. Little by little the shell slid up the embankment until at last a parapet cut straight across its line of march, the shoulder of the road, a concrete wall four inches high. As though they worked independently the hind legs pushed the shell against the wall. The head upraised and peered over the wall to the broad smooth plain of cement. Now the hands, braced on top of the wall, strained and lifted, and the shell came slowly up and rested its front end on the wall. For a moment the turtle rested. A red ant ran into the shell, into the soft skin inside the shell, and suddenly head and legs snapped in, and the armoured tail clamped in sideways. The red ant was crushed between body and legs. And one head of wild oats was clamped into the shell by a front leg. For a long moment the turtle lay still, and then the neck crept out and the old humorous frowning eyes looked about and the legs and tail came out. The back legs went to work, straining like elephant legs, and the shell tipped to an angle so that the front legs could not reach the level cement plain. But higher and higher the hind legs boosted it, until at last the centre of balance was reached, the front tipped down, the front legs scratched at the pavement, and it was up. But the head of wild oats was held by its stem around the front legs.

Now the going was easy, and all the legs worked, and the shell boosted along waggling from side to side. A sedan driven by a forty-year-old woman approached. She saw the turtle and swung to the right, off the highway, the wheels screamed and a cloud of dust boiled up. Two wheels lifted for a moment and then settled. The car skidded back on to the road, and went on, but more slowly. The turtle had jerked into its shell, but now it hurried on, for the highway was burning hot.

And now a light truck approached, and as it came near, the driver saw the turtle and swerved to hit it. His front wheel struck the edge of the shell, flipped the turtle like a tiddly-wink, spun it like a coin, and rolled it off the highway. The truck went back to its course along the right side. Lying on its back, the turtle was tight in its shell for a long time. But at last its legs waved in the air, reaching for something to pull it over. Its front foot caught a piece of quartz and little by little the shell pulled over and flopped upright. The wild oat head fell out and three of the spearhead seeds stuck in the ground. And as the turtle crawled on down the embankment, its shell dragged dirt over the seeds. The turtle entered a dust road and jerked itself along, drawing a wavy shallow trench in the dust with its shell. The old humorous eyes looked ahead, and the horny beak opened a little. His yellow toe-nails slipped a fraction in the dust.

from The Grapes of Wrath by JOHN STEINBECK

anlage: rudiments

The New Horse

'Mark,' I called and across the corral those ears perked stiff and that big head swung my way. 'Mark,' I called again and that horse turned and came about half-way and stood with head high, looking me over. I picked a coil of rope off a post and shook out a loop and he watched me with ears forward and head a bit to one side. I eased close and suddenly I snaked up the loop and it was open right for his head and he just wasn't there. He was thirty feet to the left and I'd have sworn he made it in one leap. Maybe a dozen times I tried and I didn't have a chance. The comments coming from the fence line weren't improving my temper any. Then I noticed he wasn't watching me, he was watching the rope, and I had an attack of common sense. He was wearing a halter. This wasn't any western range horse. This was one of those big eastern crossbreds with a lot of thoroughbred in them I'd heard about. Likely he'd never had a rope thrown at him before. I tossed the rope over by the fence and walked toward him and he stood blowing his nostrils a bit and looking at me. I stopped a few feet away and didn't even try to reach for the halter. He looked at me and he was really seeing me the way a horse can and I was somebody who knew his name out here where he'd been dumped out of the darkness of a box-car. He stretched that long neck and sniffed at my shirt and I took hold of the halter and that was all there was to it....

That was the beginning of my education. Yes, mister, it was me had to be taught, not that horse. The next lesson came the first time I tried to ride him. I was thinking what a big brute he was and what a lot of power was penned in him and I'd have to control all that so I used a Spanish spade bit that would be wicked if used rough. He didn't want to take it and I had to force it on him. The same with the saddle. I used a double-rig with a high-roll cantle and he snorted at it and kept sidling away and grunted all the time I was tightening the cinches. He stood steady enough when I swung aboard but when we started off nothing felt right. The saddle was too small for him and sat too high-arched over the backbone and those sloping withers. He kept wanting to drop his head and rub his mouth on his legs over that bit. At last he sort of sighed and eased out and went along without much fuss. He'd decided I was plain stupid on some things and he'd endure and play along for a while. At the time I thought he was accepting me as boss so I started him really stepping and the instant he understood I wanted him to move that was what he did. He moved. He went from a walk into a gallop in a single flowing rush and it was only that high cantle kept me from staying behind. I'm telling you, mister, that was something, the feel of those big muscles sliding smooth under me and distance dropping away under those hooves.

Then I realized he wasn't even working. I was travelling faster than I ever had on horseback and he was just loafing along without a sign of straining for speed. That horse just liked moving. I never knew another liked it as much. It could get to him the way liquor can a man and he'd keep reaching for more. That's what he was doing then. I could feel him notching it up the way an engine does when the engineer pushes forward on the throttle and I began to wonder how he'd be on stopping. I had an idea twelve hundred pounds of power moving like that would be a lot different from eight hundred pounds of bunchy little cow pony. I was right. I pulled in some and he slowed some but not much and I pulled harder and he tossed his head at the bit, biting, and I yanked in sharp and he stopped. Yes, mister, he stopped all right. But he didn't slap down on his haunches and slide to a stop on his rump the way a cow pony does. He took a series of jumps stiff-legged to brake and stopped short and sudden with his legs planted like trees and I went forward, bumping my belly on the horn and over his head and hanging there doubled down over his ears with my legs clamped around his neck. That Mark horse was surprised as I was but he took care of me. He kept his head up and stood steady as a rock while I climbed down his neck to the saddle. I was feeling foolish and mad at myself and him and I yanked mean on the reins and swung him hard to head for home and that did it. He'd had enough. He shucked me off his back the way someone might toss a beanbag. Don't ask me how. I'd ridden plenty horses and could make a fair showing even on the tough ones. But that Mark horse wanted me off so he put me off. And then he didn't bolt for the horizon. He stopped about twenty feet away and stood there watching me.

I sat on the ground and looked at him. I'd been stupid but I was beginning to learn. I remembered the feel of him under me, taking me with him not trying to get away from me. I remembered how he'd behaved all along and I studied on all that. There wasn't a trace of meanness in that horse. He didn't mind being handled and ridden. He'd been ready and willing for me to come up and take him in the station corral. But he wasn't going to have a rope slapped at him and be yanked around. He was ready and willing to let me ride him and to show me how a real horse could travel. But he wasn't going to do much of it with a punishing bit and a rig he didn't like. He was a big batch of damned good horseflesh and he knew that and was proud of it and he had a hell of a lot of self-respect. He just plain wouldn't be pushed around and that was that and I had to understand it. I claim it proud for myself that I did. I went to him and he waited for me as I knew now he would. I swung easy as I could up into the saddle and he stood steady with his head turned a little so he could watch me. I let the lines stay loose and guided him just by neck-reining and I walked him back to the ranch. I slid down there and took off the western saddle and the bridle with that spade bit. I hunted through the barn till I found a light snaffle bit and cleaned it and put it in the bridle. I held it up for him to see and he took it with no fuss at all. I routed out the biggest of the three English saddles we had for eastern dudes who wouldn't use anything else and that I'd always thought were damned silly things. I showed it to him and he stood quiet while I slapped it on and buckled the single leather cinch. 'Mark,' I said, 'I don't know how to sit one of these crazy postage stamps and I'm bunged up some from that beating. Let's take it easy.' Mister, that horse knew what I'd said. He gave me the finest ride I ever had....

from That Mark Horse by JACK SCHAEFER

Spanish spade: a sharp bladed bit that will hurt the horse on the slightest pull
cantle: rear, raised part of a saddle
cinch: strap that goes round girth of horse to hold on the saddle
horn: front raised part of a saddle on which cowboys usually keep their rope
snaffle: a jointed bit less uncomfortable to the horse's mouth

Cowboy Song

I come from Salem County
Where the silver melons grow,
Where the wheat is sweet as an angel's feet
And the zithering zephyrs blow.
I walk the blue bone-orchard
In the apple-blossom snow,
Where the teasy bees take their honeyed ease
And the marmalade moon hangs low.

My Maw sleeps prone on the prairie
In a boulder eiderdown,
Where the pickled stars in their little jam-jars
Hang in a hoop to town.

I haven't seen Paw since a Sunday
  In eighteen seventy-three
When he packed his snap in a bitty mess-trap
  And said he'd be home by tea.

Fled is my fancy sister
  All weeping like the willow,
And dead is the brother I loved like no other
  Who once did share my pillow.
I fly the florid water
  Where run the seven geese round,
O the townsfolk talk to see me walk
  Six inches off the ground.

Across the map of midnight
  I trawl the turning sky,
In my green glass the salt fleets pass
  The moon her fire-float by.
The girls go gay in the valley
  When the boys come down from the farm,
Don't run, my joy, from a poor cowboy,
  I won't do you no harm.

The bread of my twentieth birthday
  I buttered with the sun,
Though I sharpen my eyes with lovers' lies
  I'll never see twenty one.
Light is my shirt with lilies,
  And lined with lead my hood,
On my face as I pass is a plate of brass,
  And my suit is made of wood.

CHARLES CAUSLEY

Hamnavoe Market

No school today! We drove in our gig to the town.
Daddo bought us each a coloured balloon.
Mine was yellow, it hung high as the moon.
A cheapjack urged. Swingboats went up and down.

Coconuts, ice-cream, apples, ginger beer
Routed the five bright shillings in my pocket.
I won a bird-on-a-stick and a diamond locket.
The Blind Fiddler, the broken-nosed boxers were there.

The booths huddled like mushrooms along the pier.
I ogled a goldfish in its crystal cell.
Round every reeling corner came a drunk.

The sun whirled a golden hoof. It lingered. It fell
On a nest of flares. I yawned. Old Madge our mare
Homed through a night black as a bottle of ink.

George Mackay Brown

Night Hunter

The jungle is silent.
Nothing moves.
Below, a carcase.
All is in readiness.
The smell of carrion
Filled the air.

Seated on a platform.
You could almost hear his
Heart beating.
He sat there
Tense, quiet,
Motionless.
Suddenly, a tremendous roar,
Terrorises the jungle.
Panic struck
Animals scattered
Into trees and holes.
Piercing screams call out
And echo
Through the trees.
The owner of the roar?
A fearless tiger!
Running with perspiration,
The hunter shuddered
And grabbed about
For his gun.
Strained eyes peered down
From above the carcase.
All at once, a leaf rustled.
In the distance
He could still hear
Antelopes,
Taking long, lithe leaps
Into the dense forest.
Green spectral eyes
Staring upwards.
Carefully,
Oh, so carefully,

The hunter aimed.
Gradually, his finger squeezed
The trigger.
That second
A loud 'Crack'
Rang out.
After that, an even louder
'Roar'
Shook the forest.
A second 'Bang'
And all is, once again
Quiet.
Fifteen minutes passed,
And slowly
The hunter climbed down
From his hide.
He discovered a direct
Bullseye shot
In the middle of
The tiger's eyes.
He dragged
The poor beast home,
And found out that his
Male, adult
Tiger
Was seven feet long!
This brave White Hunter
Had beaten
The striped terror
Of the forest.

PENNY*

Desert

Two airmen have crashed in the desert

In times past I have loved the Sahara. I have spent nights alone in the path of marauding tribes and have waked up with untroubled mind in the golden emptiness of the desert where the wind like a sea had raised sandwaves upon its surface. Asleep under the wing of my plane I have looked forward with confidence to being rescued next day. But this was not the Sahara!

Prévot and I walked along the slopes of rolling mounds. The

ground was sand covered over with a single layer of shining black pebbles. They gleamed like metal scales and all the domes about us shone like coats of mail. We had dropped down into a mineral world and were hemmed in by iron hills.

When we reached the top of the first crest we saw in the distance another just like it, black and gleaming. As we walked we scraped the ground with our boots, marking a trail over which to return to the plane. We went forward with the sun in our eyes. It was not logical to go due east like this, for everything—the weather reports, the duration of the flight—had made it plain that we had crossed the Nile. But I had started tentatively towards the west and had felt a vague foreboding I could not explain to myself. So I had put off the west till tomorrow. In the same way, provisionally, I had given up going north, though that led to the sea.

Three days later, when scourged by thirst into abandoning the plane and walking straight on until we dropped in our tracks, it was still eastward that we tramped. More precisely, we walked east-north-east. And this too was in defiance of all reason and even of all hope. Yet after we had been rescued we discovered that if we had gone in any other direction we should have been lost. . . .

We walked on for five hours and then the landscape changed. A river of sand seemed to be running through a valley, and we followed this river-bed, taking long strides in order to cover as much ground as possible and get back to the plane before night fell, if our march was in vain. Suddenly I stopped.

'Prévot!'

'What's up?'

'Our tracks!'

How long was it since we had forgotten to leave a wake behind us? We had to find it or die.

We went back, bearing to the right. When we had gone back far enough we would make a right angle to the left and eventually intersect our tracks where we had still remembered to mark them.

This we did and were off again. The heat rose and with it came the mirages. But these were still the commonplace kind—sheets of water that materialized and then vanished as we neared them. We decided to cross the valley of sand and climb the highest dome in order to look round the horizon. This was after six hours of march in which, striding along, we must have covered twenty miles.

When we had struggled up to the top of the black hump we sat down and looked at each other. At our feet lay our valley of sand opening into a desert of sand whose dazzling brightness seared our eyes. As far as the eye could see lay empty space. But in that space the play of light created mirages which, this time, were of a disturbing kind, fortresses and minarets, angular geometric hulks. I could see also a black mass that pretended to be vegetation, overhung by the last of those clouds that dissolve during the day only to return at night. This mass of vegetation was the shadow of a cumulus.

It was no good going on. The experiment was a failure. We would have to go back to our plane, to that red-and-white beacon which, perhaps, would be picked out by a flyer. I was not staking great hopes on a rescue party, but it did seem to me our last chance of salvation. In any case, we had to get back to our few drops of liquid, for our throats were parched. We were imprisoned in this iron circle, captives of the curt dictatorship of thirst.

And yet, how hard it was to turn back when there was a chance that we might be on the road to life! Beyond the mirages the horizon was perhaps rich in veritable treasures, in meadows and runnels of sweet water. I knew I was doing the right thing by returning to the plane, and yet as I swung round and started back I was filled with portents of disaster.

from Wind, Sand and Stars by ANTOINE DE SAINT-EXUPÉRY
Translated from French by Lewis Galantière

All the Way from Scotland

I could never make up my mind if I liked Dinga. To be truthful it was easier not to, not many people did. We were in the same class at school, then we took the eleven plus. It was really the last year that I had much to do with him, the following September we went our separate ways.

Dinga was tall, fat, and he stammered. He was also very aggressive with a marked tendency to go around punching his contemporaries. He struck hard and often. It was not surprising that he was aggressive, visiting his house was like walking into a boxing gym. He was one of about ten children. They were constantly exchanging blows, even his parents joined in. The family took violence for granted.

It was Dinga who invited me, if that is the right word, to go to the castle with him to take a young pigeon from the nest. I am not sure why he asked me unless it was because I was always getting books about birds from the library. I hesitated a moment, the whole idea seemed fraught with danger. I will say, to his credit, he always gave you time to consider any proposal he made. He would listen carefully to your reply and if the answer did not meet his requirements, punch you hard in the mouth. My desire not to visit the castle was overcome by a wish to avoid a punch in the mouth.

I went home to dinner. My first thought was not to go out again. I could stay in, trouble was I would have to go out some time. I knew I would have to go to school. If we had lived in San Francisco during the earthquake we would have gone to school. I could have told my mother about Dinga but all she would have said was 'If he hits you hit him back!' She was right, but you try hitting a big fat boy.

The castle looked grimmer and shakier than ever. It was one of those castles that looked as if it had been built as a ruin. I had the feeling that the wind might blow it down. I was all for going in straight away and getting it over with, but he was more experienced at breaking the law and insisted that we should walk up and down until he was sure that no one was watching us.

I am not sure how casual I looked. First of all no one was allowed inside; secondly I was convinced it would fall down at any moment. We strolled up and down. Suddenly he gave me a push. We dashed through the fence, through a hole in the wall, and into one of the towers.

The tower was, it seemed to me, very high. There were no floors or roof, only a series of narrow ledges and steps running around inside the walls to the top. Whilst I was getting my breath back and waiting for my heart to stop pounding, Dinga the hunter was scanning the walls.

'God,' I prayed silently to myself, 'let him find a pigeon that nests near the ground.'

'There's one,' he shouted, all excited. He pointed to a hole some fifteen to twenty feet off the ground. We climbed up the steps and along the ledges until we got to it.

'I can't reach that,' I said. Suddenly, for once in my life, I was glad I was small for my age.

'Stand on my shoulders,' he said. He braced himself against the wall and I clambered up his fat body. I stood on his shoulders, accidentally, in the process, treading on his ear. I was glad when he interrupted his grunting to squeal in pain. 'Serve the fat pig right,' I thought, 'I hope he falls off the ledge on his fat head.' I forgot for a moment I was standing on his shoulders.

Slowly I straightened myself up so that I could put my hand into the hole. I was about to do this when I became rigid with fear. I couldn't move. Before my eyes flashed visions of scenes I had seen in comics and books. Pictures, quite common, of men climbers, mountaineers, clinging to the rocks at the top of peaks, their eyes wide open with terror as rampant eagles with huge claws swooped towards them defending their nests. Could you, I thought, get a rampant pigeon?

I heard Dinga shouting, or rather stuttering, like some sergeant major, 'Grab the blo . . . blo . . . blo . . . bloody thing.' I shut my eyes, plunged my hand into the hole, grabbed whatever was there, and scrambled down to the ledge. Dinga took the chick off me. He stood there, his eyes shining and his voice full of emotion. 'Look at it, it's marvellous, and it will fly all the way from Scotland.' He hid the bird under his coat and we went home on the bus.

In his back garden he had made a cage out of his sister's doll's cot. There were bars all around the sides and he had put a lid on the top. The hinges were made out of an old leather strap, and it fastened with a bolt. Around the sides of the cot were little pictures of Bo Peep, Jack and Jill, Little Boy Blue, and other nursery rhyme characters. He had tried to scrape them off, then rubbed them out with coal. The slightest suggestion that you were a bit soft could ruin your reputation as a tough guy.

He put the chick in the cage and bolted down the lid, standing back to admire both the chick and his handiwork.

'That will have to do for now, I will build a proper coop later.' I knew what he meant. It would take him a few days to steal enough wood for the pigeon loft. If Noah had built his ark in our neighbourhood, it would have been made out of other people's fencing.

Dinga fussed over the bird morning, noon, and night. He cuddled it and talked to it for hours. It didn't seem to get any bigger or stronger. The truth was he knew very little or, to be honest, nothing about the dietary habits of pigeon chicks. He fed it on everything from dried peas to bread pudding. He was annoyed with me. 'You are always reading them bird books, you ought to know what to do.' I did not try to explain that they were only about identifying them, how to recognize the golden eagle, kestrels, and so on.

The following Saturday morning he had a brainwave. He would

tie the bird by its legs to a perch in the open. It would then, he reasoned, flap its wings trying to escape. All this would build up its wing muscles until it became a kind of Tarzan of the pigeon world.

Dinga carried out his plans and we sat on the wall to watch the outcome. The bird sat on the perch. It did not move a feather, and eventually went to sleep. Dinga was not dismayed; he decided to leave it in the open. Personally, I didn't think it would have flapped its wings if you had set its feet in concrete.

When I got back after dinner I found Dinga in the garden. He was hopping mad. From what little sense I could get out of him, I learned that the family cat had killed the chick. Whilst Dinga was eating his dinner the cat, a big ugly ginger brute, had killed it and dragged it away. This information had been passed on by his sister who saw what happened but, still resentful at what he had done to her doll's cot, declined to intervene.

Dinga was getting angrier. He ran up and down the back lanes looking for the cat. He ran over the allotments. So great was his anger, he ran through old man Kelly's cabbages inviting, we believed, a certain death if caught. Finally he found it in someone's garden.

Grabbing it by the scruff of its neck he ran home. Once he got in his back garden, he grabbed a hammer. For a moment I thought he was going to hit the cat with it. He slammed the cat into the cage, slid the bolt, and nailed the lid down. The cat, when it had recovered from the shock, realized it was trapped and began to yowl and throw itself at the bars. We sat on the wall to watch.

The noise from the cat grew louder and louder. It was going berserk. The noise brought Dinga's mother on to the scene. As soon as she realized what had happened, she went mad. The truth was that she liked that mangy cat better than Dinga, and who would blame her? She had plenty of children and only one cat.

She tried to free the cat by pulling off the lid. The cat scratched her, and she threw the cage against the wall. The lid smashed open, hurling the cat to the ground. It staggered to its feet in a daze and stumbled around the garden like a drunk.

By now, Dinga was having hysterics. He was laughing that much I thought he would burst. I was laughing at him. His mother turned in her wrath towards him and charged at him like an express train. With one mighty blow she hit him off the wall. I could hear him crying and laughing at the same time.

She turned towards me. I jumped off the wall and ran.

HUGH CLARK

Mumbly-Peg

I see in the newsreels every once in a while that they're holding the national marble championships. What kind of an insanity is this? In the first place, any kid on my block who called an immie a marble would have been barred from civilized intercourse for life. In the second place, who cares who's marble champion of the *world*? The problem is, who's the best immie shooter on the block. And in the third place, they play some idiotic kind of marbles with a ring drawn in paint, and I'll bet a hat the rules are written down in a book. On my block, the rules were written down in kids. The rules were that as soon as the ground got over being frozen, any right-minded kid on the way home from school, or in recess, planted his left heel in the ground at an angle of forty-five degrees and walked around it with his right foot until there was a hole of a certain size. You couldn't measure this hole. We all knew what size the hole was supposed to be. I could go outside right now and make a hole the right size. (I did. It's still the same size. The size of an immie hole. And while I was outside I drew a line with the toe of my foot the proper distance from the hole. It's still the same distance. It isn't something you measure in feet. It's the distance from the immie hole that the line is supposed to be.) Then you stood on the line end and, to start, threw immies, underhand, at the hole. There was a kid who moved from another town who said this was 'lagging' but we didn't pay much attention to him. There's a lot more to immies. There's fins (or fens) and knucks down and whether it was fair to wiggle your feet while you were doing fins. (Or fens.) There were steelies, which were big ball bearings and could bust an immie and depending on the size of the kids these were legal or illegal, there were realies and glassies. There was the immie bag that your mother made and you put to one side because all right-minded kids carried them in a big bulge in the pocket until the pocket tore. The grownups used to talk about not playing for keeps, which was more nonsense like fathers being pals, and there was the time I owed a boy I will call Charlie Pagliaro, because that was almost his name, one hundred and forty-four immies. He played me until I had no immies, then he extended me credit, and I doubled and redoubled, and staggered home trying to absorb the fact that I owed him one hundred and forty-four immies. Now the first thing to understand is that there is no such thing as one hundred and forty-four immies. Twenty maybe, or with the help of your good friends, thirty-six, or maybe by going into servitude for the rest of your life to every kid on the whole block, you might get up to about sixty. But there is no such thing as one hundred and forty-four marbles, that's the first thing. The second is that Charlie told me he would cut my head off with his knife—which was no boy scout knife, Charlie being, believe me, no boy scout. The third thing is that I believed Charlie would do it. The fourth thing is that I believed Charlie believed he would do it. I still do. Immies were a penny apiece then.

You go to your mother and say, 'I owe Charlie Pagliaro one hundred and forty-four marbles.' Your mother says, 'I told you not to play for keeps.' You go to your father and you say, 'I owe Charlie Pagliaro one hundred and forty-four marbles.' Your father says, 'One hundred and forty-four? Well, tell him you didn't mean to go that high.'

You go to your best friend. He believes that Charlie Pagliaro will cut your head off. He lends you three immies and a steelie, which, if I remember, was worth five immies, or if big enough, ten, if the guy you were swapping with wanted a steelie at all. Two copies of *The Boy Allies* and a box of blank cartridges, a seebackroscope you got from the Johnson Smith catalogue, and a promise to Charlie Pagliaro that you will do his homework for the rest of your life, twenty-five cents in cash, and that's it. Charlie takes the stuff, and all you owe him now is fifteen immies. He knows you have a realie. Realies are worth more than diamonds. It is not a good thing to have Charlie mad at you. There goes the realie. You are alive, but poverty-stricken for all time.

from Where Did You Go? Out. What Did You Do? Nothing
by ROBERT PAUL SMITH

On My Way

The red doors show in the distance.
The wind whirls round my head.
With my head down,
and bent to one side,
I begin to jog.
The cold blitzy wind is wild and furious,
my hands red,
not able to hold my coat around me.
It dies as I walk round the corner.
My elbow jerks as I pull the door.
I let the door close,
and stand for a few seconds,
looking round.
All clear!
I run up the stairs.

STEPHEN SMITH*

Enchanted Alley

This story is set in Port of Spain, Trinidad.

Leaving for school early in the mornings, I walked slowly through the busy parts of the town. The business places would all be opening then and smells of strange fragrance would fill the High Street. Inside the opening doors I would see clerks dusting, arranging, hanging things up, getting ready for the day's business. They looked cheerful and eager and they opened the doors very wide. Sometimes I stood up to watch them.

In places between the stores several little alleys ran off the High Street. Some were busy and some were not, and there was one that was long and narrow and dark and very strange. Here too the shops would be opening as I passed, and there would be bearded Indians in loin-cloths spreading rugs on the pavement. There would be Indian women also, with veils thrown over their shoulders, setting up their stalls and chatting in a strange sweet tongue. Often I stood, too, watching them, and taking in the fragrance of rugs and spices and onions and sweetmeats. And sometimes, suddenly remembering, I would hurry away for fear the school-bell had gone.

In class, long after I settled down, the thoughts of this alley would return to me. I would recall certain stalls and certain beards and certain flashing eyes, and even some of the rugs that had been rolled out. The Indian women, too, with bracelets around their ankles and around their sun-browned arms flashed to my mind. I thought of them. I saw them again looking shyly at me from under the shadow of the stores, their veils half hiding their faces. In my mind I could almost picture them laughing together and talking in that strange, sweet tongue. And mostly the day would be quite old before the spell of the alley wore off in my mind.

One morning I was much too early for school. I passed street sweepers at work on Harris' Promenade and when I came to the High Street only one or two shop doors were open. I walked slowly, looking at the quietness and noticing some of the alleys that ran away to the backs of fences and walls and distant streets. I looked at the names of these alleys. Some were very funny. And I walked on anxiously so I could look a little longer at the dark funny street.

As I walked it struck me that I did not know the name of that street. I laughed at myself. Always I had stood there looking along it and I did not know the name of it. As I drew near I kept my eyes on the wall of the corner shop. There was no sign on the wall. On getting there I looked at the other wall. There was a sign-plate upon it but the dust had gathered thickly there and whatever the sign said was hidden behind the dust.

I was disappointed. I looked along the alley which was only now beginning to come alive, and as the shop doors opened the enchantment of spices and onions and sweetmeats emerged. I looked at the wall again but there was nothing there to say what the street was called. Straining my eyes at the signplate, I could make out a 'C' and an 'A' but farther along the dust had made one smooth surface of the plate and the wall.

'Stupes!' I said in disgust. I heard mild laughter, and as I looked before me, I saw the man rolling out his rugs. There were two women beside him and they were talking together and they were laughing, and I could see the women were pretending not to look at me. They were setting up a stall of sweetmeats and the man put down his rugs and took out something from a tray and put it into his mouth, looking back at me. Then they talked again in the strange tongue and laughed.

I stood there awhile. I knew they were talking about me. I was not afraid. I wanted to show them that I was not timid and that I would not run away. I moved a step or two nearer the wall. The smells rose up stronger now and they seemed to give the feeling of things splendoured and far away. I pretended I was looking at the wall but I stole glances at the merchants from the corners of my eyes. I watched the men in their loin-cloths and the garments of the women were full and many-coloured and very exciting. The women stole glances at me and smiled to each other and ate of the sweetmeats they sold. The rug merchant spread out his rugs wide on the pavement and he looked at the beauty of their colours and seemed very proud. He too looked slyly at me.

I drew a little nearer because I was not afraid of them. There were many more stalls now under the stores. Some of the people turned off the High Street and came into the alley and they bought little things from the merchants. The merchants held up the bales of cloth and matched them with the people's clothes and I could see they were saying it looked very nice. I smiled at this and the man with the rugs saw me and smiled.

That made me brave. I thought of the word I knew in the strange tongue and when I remembered it I drew nearer.

'Salaam,' I said.

The rug merchant laughed aloud and the two women laughed aloud and I laughed too. Then the merchant bowed low to me and replied, 'Salaam!'

This was very amusing for the two women. They talked together so I couldn't understand, and then the fat one spoke.

'Wot wrang wid de warl?'

I was puzzled for a moment and then I said, 'Oh, it is the street-sign. Dust cover it.'

'Street-sign?' one said, and they covered their laughter with their veils.

'I can't read what street it is,' I said. 'What street is this?'

The rug merchant spoke to the women in the strange tongue and the three of them giggled and one of the women said, 'Every marning you stand up dey and you doe know what they carl here?'

'First time I come down here,' I said.

'Yes,' said the fat woman. Her face was big and friendly and she sat squat on the pavement. 'First time you wark down here but every marning you stop dey and watch we.'

I laughed.

'You see 'e laughing?' said the other. The rug merchant did not say anything but he was very much amused.

'What you call this street?' I said. I felt very brave because I knew they were friendly to me, and I looked at the stalls, and the smell of the sweetmeats was delicious. There was barah too, and chutney and dry channa, and in the square tin there was the wet yellow channa, still hot, the steam curling up from it.

The man took time to put down his rugs and then he spoke to me. 'This,' he said, talking slowly and making actions with his arms, 'from up dey to up dey is Calcatta Street.' He was very pleased with his explanation. He had pointed from the High Street end of the alley to the other end that ran darkly into the distance. The whole street was very long and dusty, and in the concrete drain there was no water and the brown peel of onions blew about when there was a little wind. Sometimes there was the smell of cloves in the air and sometimes the smell of oilcloth, but where I stood the smell of the sweetmeats was strongest and most delicious.

He asked, 'You like Calcatta Street?'

'Yes,' I said.

The two women laughed coyly and looked from one to the other.

'I have to go,' I said, '... school.'

'O you gwine to school?' the man said. He put down his rugs again. His loin-cloth was very tight around him. 'Well you could wark so,' he said, pointing away from the High Street end of the alley, 'and when you get up dey, turn so, and when you wark and wark, you'll meet the school.'

'Oh,' I said, surprised. I didn't know there was a way to school along this alley.

'You see?' he said, very pleased with himself.

'Yes,' I said.

The two women looked at him smiling and they seemed very proud of the way he explained. I moved to go, holding my books under my arm. The women looked at me and they smiled in a sad, friendly way. I looked at the chutney and barah and channa and suddenly something occurred to me. I felt in my pockets and then I opened my books and looked among the pages. I heard one of the women whisper, 'Taking larning . . .' The other said, 'Aha . . .' and I did not hear the rest of what she said. Desperately I turned out my books and shook them and the penny fell out rolling on the pavement. I grabbed it up and turned to the fat woman. For a moment I couldn't decide which, but the delicious smell of the yellow wet channa softened my heart.

'A penny channa,' I said, 'wet.'

The woman bent over with the big spoon, took out a small paper-bag, flapped it open, then crammed two or three spoonfuls of channa into it. Then she took up the pepper bottle.

'Pepper?'

'Yes,' I said, anxiously.

'Plenty?'

'Plenty.'

The fat woman laughed, pouring the pepper sauce with two or three pieces of red pepper skin falling on the channa.

'Good!' I said, licking my lips.

'You see?' said the other woman, she grinned widely, her gold teeth glittering in her mouth. 'You see 'e like plenty pepper?'

As I handled my penny I saw the long brown fingers of the rug merchant stretching over my head. He handed a penny to the fat lady.

'Keep you penny in you pocket,' he grinned at me, 'an look out, you go reach to school late.'

I was very grateful about the penny. I slipped it into my pocket.

'You could wark so,' the man said, pointing up Calcutta Street, 'and turn so, and you'll come down by the school.'

'Yes,' I said, hurrying off.

The street was alive with people now. There were many more merchants with rugs and many more stalls of sweetmeats and other things. I saw bales of bright cloth matched up to ladies' dresses, and I heard the ladies laugh and say it was good. I walked fast through the crowd. There were women with saris calling out 'Ground-nuts! Parata!' and every here and there gramophones blared out Indian songs. I walked on with my heart full inside me. Sometimes I stood up to listen and then I walked on again. Then suddenly it came home to me it must be very late. The crowd was thick and the din spread right along Calcutta Street. I looked back to wave to my friends. They were far behind and the pavement was so crowded I could not see. I heard the car horns tooting and I knew that on the High Street it must be a jam session of traffic and people. It must be very late. I held my books in my hands, secured the paper-bag of channa in my pocket, and with the warmth against my legs I ran pell-mell to school.

from Sandra Street and other Stories by MICHAEL ANTHONY

barah: spiced cake made of ground lentils
channa: chick peas
dry channa is roasted
wet channa is cooked and spiced rather like curry
parata: made of dough and cooked on a hotplate like a pancake

The Tyres

Geoff and Trev were older than he was; they were at the Seniors where all the big lads were. They always seemed to know a lot more than he did and he felt they didn't really want him around when they were fooling about in the alley. But when they said they wanted some tyres he felt he had something to say.

'I know where you can get tyres,' he said.

'Where, then?' said Trev.

'Les Fletcher said he got some from the scrap-yard.'

'What scrap-yard?'

'Round by the fish shop.'

'Show us then.'

He led the way feeling proud now, like one of them and ready for anything.

The scrap-yard was only a couple of streets away and he was thinking of himself going into it and asking the man there for a couple of tyres for his pals. Les Fletcher said he'd had his for nothing.

When they got there the gates were closed and there was no sign of the old man.

'How'd you get in, kid?' said Geoff, looking up at the gate.

'It's always open when I come home from school,' he said. It sounded feeble.

''Tain't open now though, is it?' said Trev in a rough way that made him feel silly.

'Climb over,' said Geoff. The two older boys looked up and down the street and seeing there was nobody about Trev jumped up at the wall by the side of the wooden gate and got a hand-hold on one of the iron brackets that supported the barbed-wire strip running along the top of the wall. He quickly hoisted himself up and, treading very delicately, almost like a cat, eased himself above the wire and disappeared over the other side.

'Dead easy,' he shouted from over the wall.

Still there was no one about in the street but themselves. Geoff looked meaningfully at him.

'Come on then, Ekker,' he said. Eric felt suddenly proud that the older boy had used his nickname, but also scared and excited that they were going over the wall. He was afraid that somebody might come along, afraid that the scrap-yard man might turn up, that they would be caught and get into bad trouble; but also excited by the skilful way Trev had got over the wall. He wanted to be able to do it himself.

'Hurry up, kid,' said Geoff. 'After you.'

He clambered up the wall as Trev had done, getting a toe-hold and a finger-hold between the bricks where the mortar had fallen out. It hurt his fingers like mad but he couldn't give up now, so he held on tightly and stretched up with his free hand till he got hold of the rusty iron the way Trev had done. It was a tremendous pull to

get up to the top but he made it at last. He felt hot and cold at the same time with sweat on his face and the palms of his hands, and he was afraid he was going to fall when he crouched upwards to lift one leg over the barbed wire. The other side of the wall and the yard seemed much farther down than the way he had come up and he felt suddenly sick and giddy until he saw Trev come round from behind a shed.

'Wotcher, kid!' he called in a friendly way, and Eric felt he couldn't show his fear. So he stood for a second or two on top of the wall with a show of self-confidence, before leaping down, falling forward as he did so. It hurt as he grazed his hands on the gravel path.

'All right, Ekker?' said Trev, coming over to him.

''S nothin',' he said, rubbing his burning hands together.

'Still there, Geoff?' said Trev at the top of the gate.

'Copper's just come past th'end of the road,' said Geoff in a strangled voice. Eric felt his own throat tighten. His hands began to shake—a copper!

'Hey—he's come back! Oh mother! I'm off!' And they heard Geoff shuffle away. Trev turned and went round the corner of the shed. Eric followed him, hardly daring to put one foot in front of another. They both crouched, leaning on a great pile of tyres that were stacked up behind the shed. Neither of them moved. Eric found himself staring at the back of Trev's jersey and the big hole under the arm through which you could see his grubby shirt. If only we can get out again, he thought. If only I can get home. I'll never do anything like this again....

The footsteps were getting louder and nearer, and Eric imagined the policeman on the other side of the wall, just waiting for them. The footsteps stopped and then they saw that the gate was pushed and the lock rattled. Eric held his breath, expecting at any moment to see the gate open and the tall figure enter. There was silence. Both boys held themselves motionless. Then the gate was rattled again and the footsteps moved off down the street.

'Wait a bit, kid,' whispered Trev. 'In case he comes back.' Then he got on to a small stack of tyres and sat with his legs dangling over the edge.

'They'm good tyres, these,' he said, as though nothing had happened. But Eric didn't want to hear anything about tyres. The very word was like a pain to him. It seemed dangerous even to say it.

'Come on then,' said Trev. 'You go first.'

'Suppose he's still there, waiting,' said Eric, hardly able to get his words out.

'Naow, he won' be. 'E'll 've gone by now, don't you worry. 'Ain't scared, am yer?'

'No, 'course not,' he managed to say, and began to move timorously towards the wall. But as he tried to get finger-holds his courage failed him. It was as if there was no strength at all in his hands which were now throbbing from the grazes.

'Hi out, then, and let me go,' said Trev, elbowing him out of the way. Trev was soon up, his forearms resting on the top of the wall, and looking from left to right up and down the street.

'He's vamooshed,' he said. 'Come on,' and he disappeared over the wall.

A sudden panic overcame Eric and he clutched frantically at the bricks. Tears began to fill his eyes as he thought of himself there now on his own and the policeman about to return at any minute. Then he calmed himself down, wiped his eyes and looked up at the top of the wall. If Trev could do it, he could. And anyway he was braver than Geoff who had just cleared off. He reached up and found a place where the brick had partly fallen away. Then he lifted his leg as high as he could get it, wedging his toe into the ridge between the bricks and hauled himself over.

The street was empty. No sign of the policeman. Or Trev. On the top he began to get nervous and fumbled at the barbed wire, catching his hand on it. Without making sure he was clear he leapt down. His jacket was caught up in the barbed-wire and he heard the tear as he fell.

But the street was still empty. He picked himself up and without another thought ran for all he was worth up the alley. And home.

BARRY MAYBURY

Killing Whales

Eye sharpening down the line of the cannon:
The crack of the shot
                                        high whine
Aching seconds of rope
Spiralling out of the basket.

Slack rope
                    and the second, muffled explosion
Tears through bone and blubber.

Whale-back island rising from the deep,
Blow-hole like steam from a boiler.
Wild plunging
                              then rising
Resigned to the ship's tether.

Belly over in a slow-motion twist
That could be the discomfort of an itch;
Until that last, low spouting
Like brown water draining a rusty cistern.

Grapple, winch the carcass up the slope:
Out of its element the mass is grotesque.

Slice
Through the blubber to the red, hot meat.

In the ship's belly white flashes
Pattern the darkness of a sonar screen.

Circling the fleet, whales sing deeply,
Love to the hulls of factory ships.

TONY CURTIS

Wails of Musical Whales

The humpback whale, which has long been hunted by man, is an 'irrepressible composer' with a repertoire ranging from the equivalent of Beethoven to the Beatles, according to Dr Roger Payne, of the New York Zoological Society.

Dr Payne has been observing and listening to whales for more than a decade, and is convinced that the humpback whale can not only sing but compose.

Birds stay with the same song year after year but the whale is always ready to improvise with a few bars. Once one starts there is no holding the others, and the song is picked up by schools of whales as they get together off Bermuda or Hawaii.

A discerning ear can also pick out the difference between the song of a Pacific humpback whale and that of his Atlantic brother. The vocalists are usually male and tend to move their flippers slowly 'as though in time with the song', according to Dr Payne.

'We are aware of no other animals besides man in which this strange and complicated behaviour occurs. They are probably the longest, loudest and slowest songs in nature,' he said.

For the uninitiated, the songs bear more relation to noise than music, consisting mainly of 'drawn-out bass rumblings and squeaky trebles interspersed with ascending and descending scales.'

Scientists are still trying to work out why the whale behaves in this fashion. It is not known whether similar investigations are being carried out on humans.

AILEEN BALLANTYNE

The Great White Whale

Suddenly the waters around them slowly swelled in broad circles; then quickly upheaved, as if sideways sliding from a submerged berg of ice, swiftly rising to the surface. A low rumbling sound was heard; a subterraneous hum; and then all held their breaths; as bedraggled with trailing ropes, and harpoons, and lances, a vast form shot lengthwise, but obliquely from the sea. Shrouded in a thin drooping veil of mist, it hovered for a moment in the rainbowed air; and then fell swamping back into the deep. Crushed thirty feet upwards, the waters flashed for an instant like heaps of fountains, then brokenly sank in a shower of flakes, leaving the circling surface creamed like new milk round the marble trunk of the whale.

from Moby Dick by HERMAN MELVILLE

The Kra

He runs along the branches, the kra,
He carries the fruit with him, the kra,
He runs to and fro, the kra;
Over the living bamboo, the kra,
Over the dead bamboo, the kra;
He runs along the branches, the kra,
He leaps about and screams, the kra,
He permits glimpses of himself, the kra
He shows his grinning teeth, the kra.

anonymous

Mr Kandinsky explains about Unicorns

Joe is a little boy who wants a pet. His day-old chick, which he has called Kandinsky after his friend Mr Kandinsky, has died. Mr Kandinsky suggests a unicorn would make a marvellous pet.

'Every animal when it was made by the Almighty was given one extra-special present,' said Mr Kandinsky. 'The squirrel was given a wonderful tail to hold on with so he wouldn't fall from the trees; the horse was given strong fine legs so he could run fast; the lion great jaws; the elephant a trunk so he could take a shower whenever he felt like it, because an elephant is so large, how else could he keep clean? But the unicorn got the most special present of all. He was given a magic horn which could cure anything anyone was ever sick from. It could grant anybody's wish—straight off. And this horn consequently was worth £10,000 cash on sight, anywhere in the world. Don't ask me why the unicorn got this present. Someone had to get it, so why not him? Anyhow, he got it and no one else. But because of this very gift unicorns became so scarce you won't find one in the zoo, so it is in life.

'At one time unicorns were common as cart-horses, wherever you went in the streets you would see half a dozen. In those days no one was poor. You needed something so all right, you just reached out your hand and there it was, a glass of lemon tea, a new hat. Then, when people became poor, all the unicorns had their horns stolen and sold. You can imagine what that did to them. Could a lion live without his jaws, could a squirrel swing from the trees without his tail, could an elephant go on without a shower-bath, could I eat if I stopped making trousers? Of course not, so how could a unicorn live without his horn?

'Ah, Joe, they died in their thousands the lovely unicorns. They gathered together in dusty yards and at the bottom of those streets

which lead nowhere. They nuzzled one another for comfort, and closed their eyes so as not to be reminded of what they had lost. Their fine white coats became spotted, their beautiful sleek muscles slipped away into twisted sinew. They pined, they shrank, they faded, they died, and their death was sad for they had been eaten up by poverty, swallowed in the darkness of a pit with no bottom, so that no one ever saw them again.'

Mr Kandinsky sighed as he bent to throw his cold goose iron on to the gas ring. He looked at Joe with big eyes and sighed. 'This was the pity of it, my Joe,' he said. 'The unicorns passed away, but poverty was still in the world, poverty and sickness. Strong men have wasted away, beautiful girls have grown ugly, children have been lost before they could yet walk, the unicorns are all gone and yet poverty is still here. Don't ask me why. What do I know?' He sighed again, then put his hand on Joe's shoulder, pressing as to feel the small fine bone. 'Never mind,' he said, 'sometimes in spite of everything, a child grows well, a man goes from strength to strength, a woman's face does not fade. In the same way some unicorns must have lived. They were the clever ones. They saw how things were going and didn't waste time blaming men or cursing life, or threatening God, or any other foolishness. Instead they came forward and said to the rest, "Listen friends. If we don't do something soon there will be no unicorns left in the world."

'"Be quiet," some of them shouted, "can't you see we are too unhappy to do anything."

'"Don't be blasphemous," others cried, "it's the will of God."

'"Don't interrupt us when we are crying," others said, "it is the only thing left for us to enjoy."

'But some gathered together to escape, some with hope in their hearts, some with doubt, a few with the spirit which does not care either for hope or doubt. These said, "Living means waste but let who wants to live, live."

'One old unicorn who had been told about Africa when he was a baby had never forgotten. He told them, and to Africa they went that very night. In Africa they are today, although their terrible experiences made them careful about being seen by men, so that nowadays you don't see them so often. But they are even bigger now, and stronger even, and so fierce they fight at the drop of a hat. . . .'

'Could I get a unicorn into the house?' Joe asked.

'A small unicorn,' Mr Kandinsky said, 'certainly. There is no reason why a small unicorn couldn't be got into the house.'

from A Kid for Two Farthings by WOLF MANKOWITZ

Cuchulain, the Hound of Ulster

The story goes that in the old times King Conor of Ulster drew to his service a band of warriors called the Red Branch Knights. These were the best and boldest in all of Ireland. One day as he was on his travels he came across a young lad who so surprised him with his strength and cunning that he offered the boy a place in his service. At that time the king and his knights were resting at the house of Culann, the king's smith who had a ferocious hound widely known as The Hound of Ulster, and it was customary for the hound to guard the threshold of Culann's house.

While the king and his knights were carousing in the Hall, the hound outside set up a blood-chilling howl so terrible that all noise in the Hall ceased. The king, remembering that the boy had been left outside, rushed to the door, expecting the worst for once the door was closed and the hound was guarding it he would let no one pass. The lad would certainly be savaged if not killed outright. But there on the threshold, when the bolts were drawn and the doors opened, was the hound lying dead and the boy standing over it. The king and his knights stood speechless for the lad had strangled the hound with his bare hands. Culann was naturally grieved at the death of his hound and his grief was only assuaged when the boy promised to search the world to find another as fierce.

'Until then,' said the king, 'you shall be called Cuchulain, the hound of Culann.' And so it was that he received his nickname the Hound of Ulster, and grew up to be one of the most famous of Irish heroes.

anonymous

The Hound of Ulster

Little boy
Will you stop
And take a look
In the puppy shop—
Dogs blue and liver
Noses aquiver
Little dogs big dogs
Dogs for sport and pleasure

Fat dogs meagre dogs
Dogs for lap and leisure.
Do you see that wire-haired terrier?
Could anything be merrier?
Do you see that Labrador retriever?
His name is Belvoir.
  Thank you courteous stranger, said the child,
  By your words I am beguiled,
  But tell me I pray
  What lurks in the gray
  Cold shadows at the back of the shop?
Little boy do not stop
Come away
From the puppy shop.
For the Hound of Ulster lies tethered there
Cuchulain tethered by his golden hair
His eyes are closed and his lips are pale
Hurry little boy he is not for sale.

STEVIE SMITH

The Phoenix

The bird is ever fair of hue, bright with varied shades in front round the breast; green is its head behind, wondrously mingled, blended with purple. Then the tail is beautifully divided, part brown, part crimson, part artfully speckled with white spots. The wings are white at the tip and the neck green, downward and upward; and the beak gleams like glass or a jewel; bright are its jaws, within and without. Strong is the quality of its eye and in hue like a stone, a bright gem, when by the craft of smiths it is set in a golden vessel. About its neck like the round of the sun is the brightest of rings woven of feathers. Of rare beauty is the belly beneath, wondrous fair, bright and gleaming. The covering above, over the bird's back, is joined together with rich array. The legs and yellow feet are overgrown with scales. The bird is wholly peerless in aspect, like a peacock of fair growth, of which writings speak. It is not sluggish or slothful, dull nor torpid as some birds who wing their way slowly through the air, but it is speedy and swift and very alert, fair and winsome, and gloriously marked.

Translated from Old English by R. K. Gordon

Word Creature

A Fabulous New Colour

And I thought that if I could discover one thing in my life, I would like to discover a fabulous new colour—a brand-new colour that no one had ever seen before. Here's how it would be.

I would be digging in my back yard and all of a sudden while I was just casually digging, I would get this strange exciting feeling that something exceptionally good was about to happen. I would begin to dig faster and faster, my heart pumping in my throat, my hands flashing in the soft black dirt. And suddenly I would stop and put my hands up to my eyes. Because there, in the black earth, would be a ball, a perfectly round mass of this brand-new colour.

I would not be able to take it in for a moment, because I wouldn't ever have seen anything but blue and green and all, but gradually my eyes would adjust and I would see—I would be the first person in all the world to see this new colour.

I would go into the house and say to my parents, 'I have discovered a new colour,' and my parents would not be particularly interested, because there *is* no such thing as a new colour, and they would be expecting me to bring out a piece of paper on which I had mixed a lot of different water colours and made just an odd colour, and then slowly I would take my hand from my pocket and hold up the smooth round ball of new colour.

That night I would be on the news with my discovery and the announcer would say, 'Ladies and Gentlemen, if you know someone who has a colour television, go there immediately, because tonight you will see, later in our programme, a new colour, discovered today by a young boy.' And by the time I came on the television, every person in the world would be sitting in front of his set.

The announcer would say, 'Now, young man, would you tell the world how you came to discover this new colour.'

'I was outside digging in the dirt—'

'Where was this dirt?'

'Just in my back yard. And I got a strange feeling—'

'What was this strange feeling like?'

'It was the feeling that I was about to make a new and important discovery.'

'I see. Go on.'

'And I dug deeper and deeper, and then I looked down into the earth and I saw—*this*!' And I would bring forth the new colour, and all around the world a silence would occur. The only silence that had ever fallen upon the whole world at one time. Eskimoes would pause with pieces of dried fish halfway to their mouths; Russians who had run in from the cold would stop beating the snow from their arms; fishermen would leave their nets untended. And then, together, all at once, everyone in the world would say, *'Ahhhhhhhhhhh.'*

from The Midnight Fox by BETSY BYARS

If

If all the world were paper
And all the sea were ink,
And all the trees were lemon cheese,
What should we have to drink?

The Welsh Rarebit Machine

Just Suppose

1. You suddenly find yourself landed in the past (or future).
2. You can see right through walls, people, trees, etc.
3. Your legs grow very long.
4. You can become invisible at will.
5. You suddenly find yourself transported to some other place.
6. You become very small.
7. You can make the dog, or cat, talk.
8. You can turn yourself into any shape you like.
9. You suddenly discover your diet has changed to wood, metal, stone, etc.
10. You find a magic box full of . . . what?
11. You have incredible strength.
12. You can conjure things out of nothing.
13. You can change things into something else.
14. You can read other people's thoughts.
15. You can walk up walls, ceilings, etc.
16. You can see through the back of your head.
17. You can make things grow younger instead of older.
18. You can develop any skill at will for brief moments, e.g. as a cricketer, tennis player, violinist.
19. You were imprisoned in a fortress. How would you escape?
20. You can become someone else for short periods.
21. You suddenly started to eat flowers.
22. You are lost in a jungle, desert, mountains, etc.
23. Make friends with a ghost.
24. Can see into the future.
25. Can enter other people's minds and influence them.
26. Can charge yourself up with electricity and give electric shocks, or light lightbulbs, etc.
27. You have three wishes.

28 You could give food any flavour you like just by thinking about it.
29 You can rearrange your body.
30 Rebuild your head.
31 Like Orpheus you can charm things with a penny whistle.
32 You could become someone else at a particular moment in history.
33 You have a pet who can do anything you want.
34 You have magic carpet, bed, chair, bicycle, skateboard, etc.
35 You have a fantastic machine. What can it do?
36 You can breathe under water and fly in the air.
37 You were the only person in the world.
38 Everyone but you was deaf, or blind.
39 Everyone looked exactly the same.
40 You could suddenly change your age.
41 There was no school.
42 You could run very fast, jump very high, etc.
43 Everything you touched turned to gold.
44 You have the power to cast spells.
45 You are rich for a day.
46 You are king for a day.
47 You know everything.
48 You couldn't laugh.
49 You could walk on water.
50 You develop extraordinary powers. What would they be?

The Ceiling

Suppose the Ceiling went Outside
And then caught Cold and Up and Died?
The only Thing we'd have for Proof
That he was Gone, would be the Roof;
I think it would be Most Revealing
To find out how the Ceiling's Feeling.

THEODORE ROETHKE

Tenuous and Precarious

Tenuous and Precarious
Were my guardians,
Precarious and Tenuous,
Two Romans.

My father was Hazardous,
Hazardous,
Dear old man,
Three Romans.

There was my brother Spurious,
Spurious Posthumous,
Spurious was spurious,
Was four Romans.

My husband was Perfidious,
He *was* perfidious,
Five Romans.

Surreptitious, our son,
Was surreptitious,
He was six Romans.

Our cat Tedious
Still lives,
Count not Tedious
Yet.

My name is Finis,
Finis, Finis,
I am Finis,
Six, five, four, three, two,
One Roman,
Finis.

STEVIE SMITH

Charm against a Wen

Wen, wen, little wen,
Here you must neither build nor stay
But you must go north to the nearby hill
Where, poor wretch, you will find your brother.
He will lay a leaf at your head.
Under the paw of the wolf, under the eagle's wing,
Under the claw of the eagle, may you ever decline!

Shrivel like coal on the hearth!
Wizen like filth on the wall!
Waste away like water in the pail!
Become as small as a grain of linseed, and far smaller than a hand-worm's hip bone and so very small that you are at last nothing at all.

Translated from Anglo-Saxon by Kevin Crossley-Holland

wen: small wart

The Cricket Ball Charm

Now Now
little
Cricket ball
hear me as I
Speak.

Little round shiny
ball ball
With a whee
and a spin
knock those
Stumps as high
as the Sky.

William Paul Olhausen*

The Rugby Match

In these studded boots we played,
Determination made
Us run. We passed, we tripped,
We tackled, we swerved,
We sprinted—we scored!
We scrummaged, we yelled,
We tumbled, we fell,
We kicked, we hooked.
But we still lost the match.
Maybe ... because we couldn't catch!

SCOTT HARDIMAN*

Pool in the Park

I was about seven at the time and I had gone with my father to the park. It was a very big park with a large pool which always seemed to me to be a lake. There were fish in this pool and you could either fish with a net or with a rod and line. I was fascinated by the water, I remember, and I would sit on the bank and stare at it for as long as people would let me, just looking into it and trying to imagine what it would be like to move in and out of the rocks, to have a concealed place somewhere in a dark cave deep away from the light.

On this particular day, which was very warm, my father had gone walking a little way down the path as he usually did, to have a smoke probably, or to talk with some acquaintance. I was standing at the top of the bank looking at the water, absorbed as usual by its intriguing depths, when I had a sudden and overwhelming urge to dive into it, and without thinking (if I had thought, I wouldn't have done such a thing) I rushed down the bank, oblivious of everything

including the fact that I couldn't swim, and dived or fell or plunged into the water. I don't remember hitting the water but I do very clearly remember the strange, and so it seemed to me, wonderful sensation of rolling and turning about under it. I recall thinking that I was upside down and how exciting it was to see the surface of the water from underneath. I wasn't at all put out by the fact that I couldn't, presumably, breathe. I suppose all of this happened in seconds, for I was aware of my father lifting me out of the water. I can remember saying that I was all right, and I don't think that I personally was worried by the experience at all, rather the reverse, since I was preoccupied with the wonderful memory I had of being under the water.

My father carried me along the path to a hut used by the park-keeper where there was a black and rusting stove glowing with heat even though it was a warm day, and I sat naked, except for the covering afforded by my father's jacket which reached down to my ankles like the rag-and-bone man's overcoat, while my clothes dried by the stove. I was embarrassed by this, but it only seemed a few minutes before I was walking home with my father whose words I distinctly remember:

'For God's sake,' he said, wagging his finger at me, 'don't breathe a word of this to your mother, or she'll skin the backsides of both of us.' And of course I never did. It was our secret for twenty years.

PADDY KINSALE

At the Pictures

Gus was shooting pellets from a rubber band looped round fore-finger and thumb. You made them from cigarette packets or bus tickets. You could make them from any kind of paper but the heavier it was the better they flew and the more they stung when they hit.

Joby could picture the look of innocence on Gus's face as the victim looked at the back rows, trying to spot the marksman. As soon as he looked round, Gus fired again. He was an expert with a rubber band. The boy reared to his feet, turning and shouting in fury.

'Some'dy's shooting pellets back there. Give over, will you!'

The lights faded and the boy sat down again in the darkness. Joby heard a chuckle from the row behind. That Gus! You couldn't have any peace when he was around.

The attendant, a little elderly man, was moving up and down the aisles calling for quiet in a rasping voice. Joby broke the bar of treacle toffee in two and passed half to Snap. They sucked at it as the advertisements for local shops and tradespeople flashed on to the screen. This was the boring part of the show. They saw these same advertisements week after week and nobody would really settle down until the serial began.

The attendant seemed particularly keen this afternoon to get quiet in good time. Unknown to the audience, he had had an interview with the management the day before. There had been some cases of seat-slashing during Saturday matinées and he was directed now to keep order with a firm hand and to eject without argument anyone causing trouble. He was a man who enjoyed his little temporary authority and did not mean to let a crowd of unruly kids deprive him of it and the extra cash it brought in besides his full-time job.

All this was uppermost in his mind when a pellet struck him on the cheek with the force of a hornet's sting. He flashed his torch on the back rows.

'Who's firing pellets?' he demanded. 'Come on, which of you is it?'

There was no reply as the torch beam moved along the rows.

'I can put you all out, y'know,' he said belligerently.

'Ah, go and shove your head up a drainpipe,' a voice bade him from the shadows.

The torch beam played about and fell on Joby, who at that moment was grinning broadly.

'You there. Was it you?'

Joby blinked in the light of the torch, the grin gone from his face.

'Who, me?'

'Yes, you. Come on out here.'

'I haven't done owt,' Joby said.

'Come on out here or I'll come and pull you out.'

'Oh, cripes,' Joby muttered in disgust.

Gus sniggered as Joby stood up and squeezed out to the aisle.

'I don't know what you're on about,' Joby said. 'I haven't done owt.'

'We'll see about that.' The attendant took Joby by the arm. 'Come on downstairs.'

'But I'm gunna miss the serial,' Joby protested.

'You should ha' thought about that before.'

Joby was marched downstairs into the foyer. The woman in the pay-box was cashing up and there were piles of copper and silver set out in rows on the counter.

'Caught one of 'em,' the attendant said in triumph.

'I tell you I haven't done owt,' Joby said yet again.

'Let's see what you've got in your pockets,' the attendant said. 'Come on, turn 'em out.'

Joby did as he was told. It was unfortunate for him that lurking in the lining of one pocket were several pellets left over from last term when the rubber-band craze was at its height. The attendant pounced on them.

'There y'are. What's them if they're not pellets?'

'How can I shoot 'em without a rubber band?' Joby said.

'Ah, you dropped that on the floor inside,' said the attendant.

Joby fumed. He knew he couldn't win. This was grown-ups all over. Find a culprit; it didn't matter if it was the right one or not.

'I've told you it wasn't me,' Joby said. 'I've had them pellets in me pocket for weeks.'

'Are you sure it was him?' the woman in the pay-box said, looking doubtfully at Joby.

'Look, I know who it was but it wasn't me,' Joby said, appealing to her.

'Who was it, then?' she asked him.

Joby hesitated. 'I can't split, can I?'

'No, 'cos it was you,' the attendant said.

'Why don't you ask me mate, the lad I was with? He'll tell you it wasn't me.'

'Aw, he'll stick up for you, I reckon. An' anyway, I can't be messing about with you all afternoon, so you can get off home.'

'You mean I can't go back in?'

'No, you can't. And you won't get in next week, neither, if I see you first. Off you go.'

'Give us me money back, then,' Joby said.

'I don't know whether you ought to have it or not, the bother you've caused.'

'You can't refuse him his money, George,' the pay-box lady said. She took four pennies off one of the piles and passed them under the glass.

'Here you are. You've made a right mess of it, haven't you?'

Joby sensed she was sorry for him. He said, 'He's got the wrong lad, but it's no use me telling him.'

'Go on, clear off,' the attendant said, 'and don't be so cheeky.'

Joby turned away towards the entrance.

'And don't let me see you here again,' the man called after him.

For a moment Joby was consumed with anger and hatred for the little man.

'I hope you get another pellet in your earhole when you get back inside,' he said.

'Be off with you, you cheeky young devil, before I clatter your face.'

The blind, daft, stupid old keff!

Joby walked sullenly away from the cinema. He smarted at what had happened. He was no angel and he had made his share of mischief; but to carry the can back for something you hadn't done. That hurt.

from Joby by STAN BARSTOW

Shopping the Hard Way

My mother finally went to work as a cook and left me and my brother alone in the flat each day with a loaf of bread and a pot of tea. When she returned at evening she would be tired and dispirited and would cry a lot. Sometimes, when she was in despair, she would call us to her and talk to us for hours, telling us that we now had no father, that our lives would be different from those of other children, that we must learn as soon as possible to take care of ourselves, to dress ourselves, to prepare our own food; that we must take upon ourselves the responsibility of the flat while she worked. Half frightened, we would promise solemnly. We did not understand what had happened between our father and our mother and the most that these long talks did to us was to make us feel a vague dread. Whenever we asked why father had left, she would tell us that we were too young to know.

One evening my mother told me that thereafter I would have to do the shopping for food. She took me to the corner store to show me the way. I was proud; I felt like a grownup. The next afternoon I looped the basket over my arm and went down the pavement towards the store. When I reached the corner, a gang of boys grabbed me, knocked me down, snatched the basket, took the money, and sent me running home in panic. That evening I told my mother what had happened, but she made no comment; she sat down at once, wrote another note, gave me more money, and sent me out to the grocery again. I crept down the steps and saw the same gang of boys playing down the street. I ran back into the house.

'What's the matter?' my mother asked.

'It's those same boys,' I said. 'They'll beat me.'

'You've got to get over that,' she said. 'Now, go on.'

'I'm scared,' I said.

'Go on and don't pay any attention to them,' she said.

I went out of the door and walked briskly down the sidewalk, praying that the gang would not molest me. But when I came abreast of them someone shouted.

'There he is!'

They came towards me and I broke into a wild run towards home. They overtook me and flung me to the pavement. I yelled, pleaded, kicked, but they wrenched the money out of my hand. They yanked me to my feet, gave me a few slaps, and sent me home sobbing. My mother met me at the door.

'They b-beat m-me,' I gasped. 'They t-t-took the m-money.'

I started up the steps, seeking the shelter of the house.

'Don't you come in here,' my mother warned me.

I froze in my tracks and stared at her.

'But they're coming after me,' I said.

'You just stay right where you are,' she said in a deadly tone. 'I'm going to teach you this night to stand up and fight for yourself.'

She went into the house and I waited, terrified, wondering what she was about. Presently she returned with more money and another note; she also had a long heavy stick.

'Take this money, this note, and this stick,' she said. 'Go to the store and buy those groceries. If those boys bother you, then fight.'

I was baffled. My mother was telling me to fight, a thing that she had never done before.

'But I'm scared,' I said.

'Don't you come into this house until you've gotten those groceries,' she said.

'They'll beat me; they'll beat me,' I said.

'Then stay in the streets; don't come back here!'

I ran up the steps and tried to force my way past her into the house. A stinging slap came on my jaw. I stood on the sidewalk, crying.

'Please, let me wait until tomorrow,' I begged.

'No,' she said. 'Go now! If you come back into this house without those groceries, I'll whip you!'

She slammed the door and I heard the key turn in the lock. I shook with fright. I was alone upon the dark, hostile streets and gangs were after me. I had the choice of being beaten at home or away from home. I clutched the stick, crying, trying to reason. If I were beaten at home, there was absolutely nothing that I could do about it; but if I were beaten in the streets, I had a chance to fight and defend myself. I walked slowly down the sidewalk, coming closer to the gang of boys, holding the stick tightly. I was so full of fear that I could scarcely breathe. I was almost upon them now.

'There he is again!' the cry went up.

They surrounded me quickly and began to grab for my hand.

'I'll kill you!' I threatened.

They closed in. In blind fear I let the stick fly, feeling it crack against a boy's skull. I swung again, lamming another skull, then another. Realizing that they would retaliate if I let up for a second, I fought to lay them low, to knock them cold, to kill them so that they could not strike back at me. I flayed with tears in my eyes, teeth clenched, stark fear making me throw every ounce of my strength behind each blow. I hit again and again, dropping the money and the grocery list. The boys scattered, yelling, nursing their heads, staring at me in utter disbelief. They had never seen such frenzy. I stood panting, egging them on, taunting them to come and fight. When they refused, I ran after them and they tore out for their homes, screaming. The parents of the boys rushed into the streets and threatened me, and for the first time in my life I shouted at grownups, telling them that I would give them the same if they bothered me. I finally found my grocery list and the money and went to the store. On my way back I kept my stick poised for instant use, but there was not a single boy in sight. That night I won the right to the streets of Memphis.

from Black Boy by RICHARD WRIGHT

sidewalk: pavement

Anger

I was mad
Just terribly mad
I clenched my fist
My stomach rolled over
I'm red with anger
Suddenly I explode into action
I throw pencils and pens
My legs fly out at the victim
I chase him and push him on the floor
I call him names
Then I go too far
I belt out and eventually I get my revenge
I feel that I've done a good job
Although I feel a bit battered myself
I run upstairs and sulk on my bed
Next day it's all over
And forgotten.

RICHARD GRAY*

Insomnia

Aching limbs,
Shivers and sniffs,
Weary and tired,
But still very sleepless.
The hours tick by,
Until not a thing

Did stir—
The birds stopped chirping
The doors stopped slamming
The tap stopped dripping
The trees stood gaping through the open window,
The leaves stopped falling from a bold lump of timber.
Everything and anything
Was so still and quiet
That it made it hard to sleep
At such a late hour
On such a hot night.

BRENDA GRIGG*

Young Shepherd Bathing his Feet

Only the short, broad, splayed feet
Moved...

Feet that had trodden over
Soft soil,
Sand,
Ploughed veld,
Mountain rocks
And along narrow tracks,
On Winter clay and
Dust of
Summer roads...

The short, broad, splayed feet
Moved
In and out...

The stumpy toes stretched wide
Apart
And closed together
Then opened wide...

In ecstasy.

PETER CLARKE

Little Dolly Daydream

Her mother's out today,
the house is quiet as a dozing mouse,
the cat meows and curls to sleep.

Upstairs she stands before the glass,
arms on hips, she struts this way and that.

Laid out beneath the looking-glass are jars or boxes,
bottles, aerosols and plastic packs.

She has an hour to try on all the scents,
to puff the clouding powder, smear the cream
and draw whatever feature her changing fancy takes.

The placid pool invites, and plunging in dissolves
her ordinary self—the bitten nails, the grimy neck,
the whisps of wayward hair.

She lifts the little brush and gently strokes,
stardusts the tickling eyelids with some silver flakes,
daubs in bow lips and high-arched brows.

Deftly, having watched, sticks lashes,
Drooping minute frayed bats' wings,
glistens lipsalve, reddens cheeks.

She turns her pale child's face
into all the faces she has seen
in the darker mirrors of her mind.

Stringing out her loosening strands of hair,
she transforms herself into a witch,
the Snow White Queen,
La Belle Dame Sans Merci,
a coyly smiling Columbine.

And, from lurking deeps beyond the silver wall,
she conjures, unaware,
the many quickly-fading future selves
the unkind glass conceals.

Paddy Kinsale

Phizzog

This face you got,
This here phizzog you carry around,
You never picked it out for yourself, at all, at all—did you?
This here phizzog—somebody handed it to you—am I right?
Somebody said, 'Here's yours, now go see what you can do with it.'
Somebody slipped it to you and it was like a package marked:
'No goods exchanged after being taken away'—
This face you got.

CARL SANDBURG

The Chinese Queen

Proud and tall, with a face so white,
Sapphires gleaming and diamonds bright,
Pointed nails, and staring eyes,
A face so cruel, but a mind so wise.

Silk and velvet robes she does wear
And a crown of jewels on her black hair.
Treasure chambers full of gold,
These all belong to the queen so old.

JULIA*

Tutankhamen

The horrible look
The staring death
The blue and gold stripes
The terrible death
What was it like,
The terrific gold mask
The liking of a blue sea.

The incredible piece of work
keeping him together.
The sad face.
The love, the happiness and the shame.
What was he thinking I wonder,
The young boy dead only
Fifteen years old.

JONATHAN REYNOLDS*

An Epitaph

Here lies a most beautiful lady,
Light of step and heart was she;
I think she was the most beautiful lady
That ever was in the West Country.
But beauty vanishes; beauty passes;
However rare—rare it be;
And when I crumble, who will remember
This lady of the West Country?

WALTER DE LA MARE

Time

The woods decay, the woods decay and fall,
The vapours weep their burden to the ground,
Man comes and tills the field and lies beneath,
And after many a summer dies the swan.

from Tithonus by ALFRED LORD TENNYSON

Rogues and Vagabonds

Behind the railway seeds have flown
and sprung between the iron and stone.
Nettles grow thick enough to mask
hideaways where sleepers bask
and heavy smells of green and seed
of cowparsley and river weed
mixed with railway dirt and dust
diesel fumes and flakes of rust
mingle in the grassy den
with the closer stench of men
stretched in odd shapes, sunburned, still
lords of the jungle with time to kill.
And poking the green film on the river
abandoned bottles set for ever.

PATIENCE TUCKWELL

Desolate Line

D Damp moss on the rocks,
E Empty rocky cutting,
S Sandy dust in the air,
O Old crooked trees,
L Lines rusty and old,
A All unused for many years,
T Trains not running anymore,
E Enticing children with their mighty roar.

L Long wait to be opened again,
I Industrious line at one time,
N Now all closed down,
E Engulfed by weeds on the cuttings side.

WARREN BRINDLEY*

Tramp

He liked he said
rainbows in the sky
and children
who passed him in the
street
without staring.
And he liked he said the
ordinary things
like
roses in snow
and the way he
remembered
the first time
the first time he
really smelt the
rain on
a green hillside
back home
just before the sun died.
And he liked he said
thinking about
who slept beneath the red
brick roofs he
walked by in the
early part of the day
from Lands End to John O' Groats.
But he said
as a full time tramp with no
other place to go he
was worried
where he would die—
Lands End or John O' Groats.

WILLIAM MARSHALL

A Lonely Person

I sat in my house
Alone.
Looking through the window all day,
All day.
Not a knock
Or a blow.
What's that?
Only the wind
Blowing its powerful breeze,
So lonely as I started to cry
I beg you, dear Lord,
Let me have one,
Just one, visitor,
That will take an interest in me.

LOUIE WILKES*

The Moated Grange

With blackest moss the flower-plots
   Were thickly crusted, one and all:
The rusted nails fell from the knots
   That held the pear to the garden-wall.
The broken sheds looked sad and strange:
   Unlifted was the clinking latch;
   Weeded and worn the ancient thatch
Upon the lonely moated grange.

from Mariana by Alfred Lord Tennyson

The Way through the Woods

They shut the road through the woods
  Seventy years ago.
Weather and rain have undone it again,
  And now you would never know
There was once a road through the woods
  Before they planted the trees.
It is underneath the coppice and heath,
  And the thin anemones.
  Only the keeper sees
That, where the ring-dove broods,
  And the badgers roll at ease,
There was once a road through the woods.

Yet, if you enter the woods
  Of a summer evening late,
When the night-air cools on the trout-ringed pools
  Where the otter whistles his mate,
  (They fear not men in the woods,
  Because they see so few.)
You will hear the beat of a horse's feet,
  And the swish of a skirt in the dew,
Steadily cantering through
  The misty solitudes,
As though they perfectly knew
  The old lost road through the woods. . . .
But there is no road through the woods.

RUDYARD KIPLING

Lake Segden

No one writes about this lake and it is spoken of only in whispers. As though to an enchanted castle, all roads to it are barred and over each one hangs a forbidding sign—a plain, blunt straight line.

Man or beast, faced by that sign, must turn back. Some earthly power has put that sign there; past it none may ride, none may walk, crawl or even fly.

Guards with swords and pistols lurk beside the path in the nearby pine-grove.

You may circle and circle the silent wood searching for a way through to the lake, but you will find none and there will be no one to ask, for no one goes into this wood. They have all been frightened away. Your only chance to venture through will be one afternoon in the rain along a cattle track, in the wake of the dull clink of a cowbell. And from your first glimpse of it, vast and shimmering between the tree-trunks, you know before you reach its banks that you will be in thrall to the place for the rest of your life.

Segden Lake is as round as though traced out with a pair of compasses. If you were to shout from one side (but you must not shout or you will be heard), only a fading echo would reach the other bank. It is a long way across. Woods immure the lakeside entirely, a dense forest of row upon unbroken row of trees. Coming out of the wood to the water's edge, the whole of the forbidden shore can be seen: here a strip of yellow sand, there a grey stubble of reeds, there a lush swathe of grass. The water is smooth, calm and unruffled, and apart from some patches of weed by the shore the white lake-bed gleams through the translucent water.

A secret lake in a secret forest. The water looks up and the sky gazes down upon it. If there is a world beyond the forest it is unknown, invisible; if it exists it has no place here.

Here is somewhere to settle for ever, a place where a man could live in harmony with the elements and be inspired.

But it cannot be. An evil prince, a squint-eyed villain, has claimed the lake for his own: there is his house, there is his bathing-place. His evil brood goes fishing here, shoots duck from his boat. First a wisp of blue smoke above the lake, then a moment later—the shot.

Away beyond the woods the people sweat and heave, whilst all the roads leading here are closed lest they intrude. Fish and game are bred for the villain's pleasure. There are traces where someone lit a fire; but it was put out and he was driven away.

Beloved, deserted lake.

My native land....

ALEXANDER SOLZHENITSYN
Translated from Russian by Michael Glenny

The Old Lock Factory

It was the sudden silence you noticed first. Outside it had been the noise of lorries, the repeated banging of the dropforgings and the constant rachetting of machinery that seemed to be everywhere round Albion Street and Erebus Road. But inside the old factory the noise was stopped or suspended; perhaps it was still there only deadened by the thick walls and the heavy wooden beams. For years the place had been abandoned and anything worth having had long been ripped out—benches, or iron, or lead from the roofs. Other intruders had left ugly holes here and there in the inner walls, and a few cobweb-covered windows had been smashed, but still the place seemed much as it might have been a long time ago. There was a smell about it of iron-filings and slurry, and the floor still had that greasy feel of earth mixed with swarf and oil.

We had broken into the place through the fence that backed on to the canal, determined to have some fun in the old lock shop, but the strangeness of the place had unsettled us as though it might be inhabited by the ghosts of long-departed workmen with oily leather-aprons and the bony forearms of the sharp-eyed humpy men who had filed away their lives here. We walked about swaggering uneasily, kicking up rubble or pulling futilely at a piece of rusted chain bolted into the wall, we looked up to the blackened roof and the heavy crossbeams and wondered nervously whether we might climb up there, but it was high and dark and we thought better of it. The place was clammy, too quiet, and too inhospitable, and it had smothered our desire even to attack it. We left the silence to itself and moved away sheepishly towards the canal. And then, yelping like fiends, we made for the Common, where the air was clearer.

PADDY KINSALE

Disappearance

Total disappearances—where a human being just vanishes from the face of the earth without explanation—have always interested me. And here is perhaps the strangest that ever came my way. For it seems to involve a different kind of space to the ordinary space we are familiar with. It was told to me by a farmer from Texas, a fellow I met in 1891 or 2 when I had a dairy farm in Ontario.

With his mother and a younger brother he ran a farm in a rather isolated part of the State. One evening in winter, after a snowfall that had lasted all day, the wind shifted, the clouds vanished, and a full moon blazed down on the carpet of fresh snow. In that clear, dry air, it was almost bright enough to read; and the mercury shot down to below zero. It was while preparing supper that the mother, needing water, asked Jim, the younger of the two brothers, to fetch some from the well. This was a daily commonplace job. The well, their only house-supply, never ran dry. And Jim, putting on his fur mitts and cap, sallied out with a couple of pails as usual. The distance to the well was about 150 yards. But the lad did not come back, and his brother, who told me the story, went out himself to see what was the matter. No question of danger arose. None was possible. There on the otherwise untrodden snow were Jim's foot-marks, clear as daylight, the only tracks visible. And there, about half-way to the well, lay the two pails on the ground. Following the tracks, he reached them. They stopped dead beside the pails. No track of any kind was visible along the farther fifty yards to the well.

It was mysterious to say the least. The snow lay quite smooth and undisturbed. No sign of flurry or disturbance. He shouted his brother's name. No answer came. It frightened him, for no conceivable explanation came to him. For the first time in his life, he told me, he was aware of goose-flesh. Then, hurrying back to the house to consult with his mother, he heard a faint voice: 'Help! Help me!'

It was Jim's voice beyond all question. It seemed to come from the air. His mother, when she rushed out, heard it too. But though they both stood there shouting and shouting, and Jim's voice, now fainter, now louder, now close, now far away, answered, they could never decide exactly the direction it came from. Indeed, it seemed to come from all directions, though always from the empty air about them, and never from below.

The neighbours heard it too next day when the older brother had ridden out to fetch them. All came from several miles away, so isolated was the farm. No explanation was forthcoming. Jim never came back. He was never seen again. As the winter passed the voice grew fainter, but hardly a day went by without the cry for help being heard. It was an event of the first, even of shattering importance, to the whole country. With the warming up of the spring days, though still audible, the cry seemed fainter and fainter, more and more distant, till finally in the great heats of the Texan summer it died away completely and was never heard of again.

ALGERNON BLACKWOOD

Short Ghost Story

The last man alive on earth sat alone in his house. Suddenly the front door bell rang . . .

A Ghost Story

The Roman author Pliny writes to a friend.

In Athens there was a large and roomy house which was deserted. No one would live there because in the middle of the night could be heard the rattling and clanking of chains, first distantly and then closer. Then a spectre appeared in the form of an old man, thin and wizened with filthy rags, unkempt hair and straggling beard, and wearing fetters on his legs and chains on his hands. Naturally the people who lived close by were unable to sleep and in despair at the recurring apparition. Eventually a notice was put up on the house offering it for sale at a very low price.

About this time a visitor came to the city, a man called Athenodorus, a philosopher. He read the notice and was quite taken with the place, though, of course, he was suspicious of the low price. Yet when he found out the reason he was more than ever interested and decided to rent the house.

When it got dark he ordered a bed to be made up for him in the front part of the house and asked for his writing materials and a lamp to be set by the side of his bed. Then he told his servants to leave him, and concentrated on his writing.

For a time nothing happened, then there came a rattling and clanking of chains. Athenodorus took no notice and kept on writing. The noise became louder, then quieter and then louder again, first in one place and then in another until it was almost deafening, and the philosopher was compelled to look up. There was the ghost just as it had been described to him, standing close by and beckoning with its finger. Athenodorus stared at it for a while and then resumed his writing, but the ghost angrily shook its chains and beckoned to him again. So he set down his stylus quite calmly, took up his light and followed the ghost. It moved very slowly and awkwardly as though burdened by the heavy chains. Then, when it reached the courtyard, it suddenly disappeared. Athenodorus put down his light and collected a little pile of grass leaves to mark the spot.

The next day he sent for the magistrates and advised them to have the spot excavated. There they found a skeleton bound with rusty iron chains. The bones were taken and buried in a proper graveyard, and after that the ghost was never seen again.

from The Letters of Pliny, freely translated from Latin

The Argument

If you push your way through the thick grass, past the tall, tall silver blue trees whose tops reach up several miles through the atmosphere to reach the cosmic rays which hurl themselves at the planet from the dying sun, you will come to a strange building, spinning about a foot above the grasses. You might wonder what strange phenomenon keeps this heavy metal structure in the air, but it is perfectly natural: the dying sun and dying planet have reduced the gravity so that, if an object is set spinning, it will remain spinning above the surface of the Earth.

There were only about five million people left on the smaller Earth now. All the others had taken the space ships out to the far off stars, to find new planets and make new Earths round a younger sun. But a spaceship hadn't left or come to Earth for about 200 years and the old stations were derelict and full of superstition. Nothing grew there because of the launching; and so by the almost heathen inhabitants of Earth they were considered places of death to be completely avoided. One family living on this lost Earth was the Jones family. The parents were typical of Earth inhabitants at that time; they were narrow-minded and rather lazy as they were living off the canned supplies of the old Earth and had no care of the future. They lived in their spinning dome oblivious of any goings on around them. They lived no social life and didn't know the meaning of morality. Nor did they know they were soon going to die a long predicted death.

Their one son was different; he didn't fit in with their way of life at all. Most of the time he lived on the ground, camping around and eating any tubers or berries he could find. By our standards he would be considered average if not slightly a weakling with small muscles. But then, with the decreased gravity, he would be considered strong and muscular. He also had an alert mind. In his youth he has befriended an old starman. This man could remember Earth and its distant colonies in all their glory (extreme old age was inevitable when travelling weightless between the stars). He taught Matt how to fly spaceships and secretly showed him a small vessel he had ready to fly away in. It was fully atomized. He need just press the starting button and they would be away off to the stars. But the old man died before he had the chance.

Now Matt dreamed of flying off to the prosperous civilized planet that the ship was programmed to fly to. Things were getting worse on Earth; on some days you couldn't even see the sun in the sky and all the vegetation was dying off and there was hardly any wildlife. The seas were barren.

Today it was exceptionally hot. The sun looked explosive. It seemed the right day to tell his parents they were leaving.

He leapt up into the revolving house. The doorway was hard to miss when you had so much spring, through lack of gravity, and inside the sensation wasn't one of movement, as inside the first dome was another, revolving at such a pitch, that all sense of movement was lost.

The parents were obviously surprised to see their son because they stopped eating, fingers and tongues poised.

The house stank. It was filthy; discarded food tins lay in every corner. There were three rooms. The other two rooms were locked but the parents couldn't be bothered to find the key or look for another house.

'Mother and Father,' stated Matt loudly, 'it has come to my notice that this planet is dying with the sun. It's about time we left. I know where a perfectly good spaceship is and how to control it so we can leave today.'

The father stared expressionlessly for a moment, then opened his mouth, revealing the remains of a meal and several black teeth, and laughed raucously. The mother gave a slight, simpering sneer in sympathy. Matt got angry. He slammed his fist down on the table.

'I'm being serious,' he yelled. 'Go out there and look at the sun. It's going to explode, any minute even!!'

No one moved.

'Look you. . . .'

His father cut him short by lifting up his hand, then said in a quiet calm voice.

'We've lived on this planet for sixty years and no suns have exploded yet so I don't see why they should now.'

He looked fixedly at Matt, then began to chuckle at this joke. He became serious again.

'We've been faithful to this planet and she bears us no malice. The trouble with you is you think too scientifically.'

'And the trouble with you is you don't think scientifically enough. It's got nothing to do with the poor little Earth. She's going to explode whether she likes it or not, and you with her if you don't come with me.'

'Look, son, we are not going and neither are you for that matter.'

Matt tried new tactics.

'I am. I'm off now.'

A wail came from Mother.

'Oh, I understand now. You're going to leave us here so that when we get old we will starve to death. I understand you. You don't care about your parents who laboriously brought you up or about the planet which has supported you during your childhood; the planet you played on and loved.'

The tears were running down her cheeks. The wrong tactics. Matt stood appalled as the scene continued:

'I know what will happen if we let you take us to that place. You will leave us there to get lost and have the curse that is there kill us. And even if we do get on one of these legendary spaceships, it won't go. How can it? The magic ended long ago.'

'But it's not magic.'

'How else can something just disappear like that. You say we are going to die; to come with you would be certain death.'

'No, it wouldn't, it couldn't. You've got to come with me, got to.' He looked at their silent faces, then leapt from the house and began to run towards the space port. Father stood at the door and shouted at him to come back at once. Matt blocked his ears and ran faster. He looked silently out of the viewport at a weak distant spot of light that was Earth's sun. Suddenly, as he was watching, it flared up consuming all the darkness around it, then died away quickly, leaving a black emptiness staring at him like an accusing dead eye.

EVE RYAN*

Eyes of Night-Time

On the roads at night I saw the glitter of eyes:
my dark around me let shine one ray; that black allowed
their eyes: spangles in the cat's, air in the moth's eye shine,
mosaic of the fly, ruby-eyed beetle, the eyes that never weep,
the horned toad sitting and its tear of blood,
fighters and prisoners in the forest, people
aware in this almost total dark, with the difference,
the one broad fact of light.

Eyes on the road at night, sides of a road like rhyme;
the floor of the illumined shadow sea
and shallows with their assembling flash and show of
sight, root, holdfast, eyes of the brittle stars.
And your eyes in the shadowy red room,
scent of the forest entering, various time
calling and the light of wood along the ceiling
and over us birds calling and their circuit eyes.
And in our bodies the eyes of the dead and the living
giving us gifts at hand, the glitter of all their eyes.

MURIEL RUKEYSER

It is Night

It is night
and the stars
Hang loosely in the sky.
As if
at any moment
the slender thread might break
and they would fall.
Making a heap of light in the dark street.

JANICE E. PARKIN

List of Illustrations

Acknowledgements

Michael Anthony: From *Sandra Street and Other Stories.* Reprinted by permission of André Deutsch Ltd; **Richard Bach:** Extract from *Jonathan Livingstone Seagull.* Reprinted by permission of Turnstone Press Ltd; **Aileen Ballantyne:** From *The Guardian,* May 30, 1979. By permission; **Stan Barstow:** Extract from *Joby.* Reprinted by permission of Michael Joseph Ltd; **Robert Bernen:** From *Tales from the Blue Stacks.* Reprinted by permission of Hamish Hamilton Ltd; **Algernon Blackwood:** 'Disappearances'. Reprinted by permission of the Estate of Algernon Blackwood and A. P. Watt Ltd; **Betsy Byars:** From *The Midnight Fox.* Reprinted by permission of Faber and Faber Ltd; **Charles Causley:** From *Union Street* (Granada Publ. Ltd). Reprinted by permission of David Higham Associates Ltd; **John Clare:** 'The Fox' © Eric Robinson 1967 and first published by Oxford University Press in *Selected Poems and Prose of John Clare* chosen and edited by Eric Robinson and Geoffrey Summersfield. 'Dew Drops' © Eric Robinson 1981. By permission of Curtis Brown Academic Ltd; **Hugh Clark:** From *The Guardian,* 26 January 1980. By permission; **Peter Clarke:** From *Poems from Black Africa,* edited by Langston Hughes. © 1963 by Langston Hughes. Reprinted by permission of Indiana University Press; **J. A. Connor:** From *With Love Somehow* (O.U.P. 1962). By permission of the author; **Kevin Crossley-Holland:** From *Battle of Malden and Other Anglo-Saxon Poems* (Macmillan). Reprinted by permission of the author and Deborah Rogers Ltd Literary Agency; **Tony Curtis:** From *Album* (Wales, 1974 Christopher Davies Ltd). By permission of the author; **Emily Dickinson:** Reprinted by permission of the publishers and the Trustees of Amherst College from *The Poems of Emily Dickinson,* edited by Thomas H. Johnson, Cambridge, Mass; The Belknap Press of Harvard University Press, Copyright 1951, © 1955, 1979 by the President and Fellows of Harvard College, **R. K. Gordon:** 'The Phoenix' from *Anglo-Saxon Poetry,* edited and translated by R. K. Gordon (Everyman's Library). Reprinted by permission of J. M. Dent and Sons Ltd; **Robert Horan:** From *Beginning* (1949, Yale Series of Younger Poets: No. 46). By permission of Yale University Press; **Paul Hyland:** 'Farrier's Dog' first broadcast on *Poetry Now,* BBC Radio 3. Also in *Poetry Review.* Reprinted by permission of the author; **P. J. Kavanagh:** From *Life Before Death.* Reprinted by permission of Chatto and Windus Ltd for the author; **Rudyard Kipling:** Extract from 'The Way Through The Woods' from *Collected Poems.* Reprinted by permission of A. P. Watt Ltd. for the National Trust and Macmillan, London, Ltd; **Philip Larkin:** From *the North Ship.* Reprinted by permission of Faber and Faber Ltd; **Laurie Lee;** From *Cider with Rosie.* Reprinted by permission of The Hogarth Press Ltd for the author; **George Mackay Brown:** First broadcast on *Poetry Now,* BBC Radio 3. Printed here by permission of the author; **Roger McGough:** From *In the Glassroom,* copyright © 1976 by Roger McGough. Reprinted by permission of Hope Leresche and Sayle; **Wolf Mankowitz;** From *A Kid for Two Farthings* (1953). Reprinted by permission of André Deutsch Ltd; **Walter de la Mare:** From *Collected Poems* (Constable). Reprinted by permission of The Literary Trustees of Walter de la Mare and The Society of Authors as their representative; **William Marshall:** From *New Poetry 14* (Workshop Press Limited). Reprinted by permission of the author; **Liam O'Flaherty:** From *The Short Stories of Liam O'Flaherty.* By permission of Jonathan Cape Ltd for the author; **William Paul Olhousen:** 'The Cricket Ball Charm' from *Children as Writers, 6.* Reprinted by permission of Heinemann Educational Books; **Janice Parkin:** From *T.A.S.C. Poetry.* Reprinted by permission of the editor; **Jonathan Reynolds.** 'Tutankhamen' from *Children As Writers, 6.* Reprinted by permission of Heinemann Educational Books; **Theodore Roethke:** From *Collected Poems.* Reprinted by permission of Faber and Faber Ltd; **Muriel Rukeyser:** From **The Green Wave** (Doubleday 1948) and also in *The Collected Poems of Muriel Rukeyser* (McGraw Hill, 1979), copyright 1948, © 1976. Reprinted by permission of Monica McCall, International Creative Management; **Antoine de Saint-Exupéry:** From *Wind, Sand and Stars,* translated by Lewis Galantiers. Reprinted by permission of William Heinemann Ltd; **Carl Sandburg:** From *Good Morning, America,* copyright 1928, 1956 by Carl Sandburg. Reprinted by permission of Harcourt Brace Jovanovich Inc.; **Jack Schaefer:** From *The Pioneers* (1957). Reprinted by permission of André Deutsch Ltd; **Chris Searle:** Extract from *The Forsaken Lover: White Words and Black People* (1972). Reprinted by permission of Routledge and Kegan Paul Ltd; **Stevie Smith:** From *The Collected Poems of Stevie Smith* (Allen Lane). Reprinted by permission of James MacGibbon Executor; **Alexander Solzhenitsyn:** From *Stories and Prose Poems,* translated by Michael Glenny, Reprinted by permission of M. Claude Durand and the Bodley Head; **Alexander Johnston Sorely:** 'My Poem' from *Children As Writers, 6.* Reprinted by permission of Heinemann Educational Books; **John Steinbeck:** From *The Grapes of Wrath.* Reprinted by permission of William Heinemann Ltd; **Wallace Stevens:** From 'Tattoo' from *Collected Poems.* Reprinted by permission of Faber and Faber Ltd; **May Swenson:** From *New and Selected Things Taking Place,* copyright © 1956 by May Swenson. First appeared in the *New Yorker.* By permission of Little, Brown and Co. in association with the *Atlantic Monthly Press;* **Charles Tomlinson:** From *Written on Water,* © Oxford University Press 1972. Reprinted by permission of the author and Oxford University Press; **Patience Tuckwell:** From *New Poetry 21* (Workshop Press Ltd). Reprinted by permission of the author; **Arthur Waley:** From *Chinese Poems.* By permission of George Allen and Unwin (Publ.) Ltd; **Richard Wright:** From *Black Boy.* Reprinted by permission of Jonathan Cape Ltd. for Mrs. Ellen Wright. The editor would also like to thank the following for permission to reprint their poems: Birmingham Education Committee for 'Night Hunter' by Penny (aged 11 years) from *Birmingham Children Write* (1970); Warren Brindley for 'Desolate Lines'; The Headmaster, Hattersley Comprehensive School for 'Rain' by Stuart Bridges, 'The Wooden Stage' by Carl Murray, and 'On My Way' by Stephen Smith; The Headmaster, St. John's Middle School, Blakebrook, Kidderminster for 'The Rugby Match' by Scott Hardiman; Manchester Education Committee for 'The Roadmen' by Brian Poole and 'A Lonely Person' by Louie Wilkes both from *Early Lines,* and for 'The Argument' by Eve Ryan from *Prospects.* The publishers have made every effort to trace copyright holders, but in some cases without success, and apologise for any infringement of copyright.

In the compilation of these and earlier books I am grateful for much useful advice and help from editors and friends—principally Mary Worrall, Alison Souster and Martin Raynor, my wife Joan, and Jerry Rowlands who, over the years, has brought to my attention some splendid bits of poetry and prose. Especially I am grateful to my early colleagues, Geoffrey Summerfield and Paddy Creber and to students at Summerfield, Shenstone and North Worcestershire Colleges; also to many schools, teachers and friends in and around Worcestershire for advice, ideas, and for letting me try out material with their classes, and of course, most important of all, pupils I have encountered in schools or whose work I have used.

Thematic Index